Evolution's Hand

Evolution's Hand
Searching for the Creator in Contemporary Science

JOHN CAFFERKY

EAST END BOOKS
Toronto 1997

Printed in Canada by Metrolitho

Canadian Cataloguing in Publication Data

Cafferky, John, 1955 –
   Evolution's hand : searching for the creator in contemporary science

Includes bibliographical references and index.
ISBN 1-896973-00-0

1. Evolution (Biology) - Philosophy.   2. Natural theology.
3. Science - Philosophy.   4. Religion and science.   I. Title.

QH366.2.C32 1997   576.8'01   C97-931136-5

East End Books is an imprint of Venture Press
45 Fernwood Park Avenue
Toronto, Canada
M4E 3E9
(416) 691-6816

CONTENTS

*Dedicated
to Mary*

ACKNOWLEDGEMENTS

An enterprise of this sort is bound to be contentious and challenging, and authors who attempt such things need all the help they can get. I owe an unending debt of gratitude for the patience, understanding, and unqualified support and encouragement of my dear friend Father Michael Hughes. Thank you so much – I will never forget.

Many others have helped and contributed in seeing this project through. Special thanks to Meta and Kevin Hannifin, to Fergus Devereaux for reading and editing the early manuscript as well as for his helpful comments on the final work, to Dr. Brian Spence for reading the final manuscript and making helpful suggestions, to Jim Wagner for his generous artistic advice on the cover, to Drew Meikle for his advice and suggestions, to Pat Cafferky for reading the earliest draft of this work and for his extensive comments, to Brian Horgan for reading the manuscript and making useful comments, and to Steve Dunne for taking the time to read an early draft of the work.

I am indebted as well to my congenial and hard-working literary colleagues at East End Books: Randall White, Nadine Stoikoff, Jeanne MacDonald, and Andy Tong, who have believed that this particular book deserves a hearing and, to this end, have given of their time and effort in a generous and professional spirit.

Finally, but certainly not least, I owe everything to my wonderful wife, Bridjette. She saw the work through from conception to completion with unwavering optimism and encouragement – thank you.

INTRODUCTION

On the Archaean Rock of the Canadian Shield

"Does God exist?" is the ultimate philosophical question. And it is also the ultimate subject of this book – the central preoccupation that underlies everything else.

The daunting task of undertaking, as it were, scientific research on so vast a subject first entered my mind a decade or so ago while I was working as chief geologist for Agnico Eagle Mines at their Joutel gold operation on the Canadian Shield, in northwestern Quebec. The deposit we were working was in a suite of very ancient or 'Archaean' rocks more than 2 billion years old. It soon became apparent that this deposit had quite an unusual fascination for us, since it bore all the markings of a 'syngenetic' origin; the metal sulphides in the host-rock, in other words, were contemporaneous with the rock itself.

Normally, rocks of this age would be heavily scarred from later deformations in their geological history, and it would be almost impossible to identify the origin of the ore. But, by chance, the Joutel deposit was extremely well-preserved. The beds of sulphide could easily be identified. And this attracted a great many visiting geologists from North America and around the world. I eventually had the pleasure of playing host to well over a thousand fascinated colleagues. Collectively, we were nearly unanimous in agreeing that the pristine Joutel deposit was syngenetic in origin.

This conclusion had an immediate interest for my work as a mining geologist. It also provoked some deeper and rather troubled reflections during my spare moments in the northern wilderness. If the deposits of the very ancient Archaean period of geological history were syngenetic, then the waters of our planet's very ancient environment must have been saturated in metals and other minerals. If this were true, then how could we account for the origin of life on the conventional 'reductionist' principles that have dominated scientific thinking on the subject since the work of Charles Darwin in the nineteenth century? The essential building blocks of life in this sense, after all, are pure chemicals. How could pure chemicals be extracted from an environment that was heavily contaminated with a multitude of other mineral species – as conventional reductionist principles would require?

There isn't a lot to do in your spare time at a mining site, and this tends to prompt reflective habits of mind. The more I pursued this train of thought, the more troubled I became.

Phosphorous is critical for life, for example, but it is a minor element of the Earth's crust with less than one percent occurrence. The ancient rocks of the crust also have no significant accumulation of phosphate minerals, even though most of the elements with which phosphorous forms minerals were abundant in the Archaean environment.

One just has to think of the mountains of iron ore in ancient rocks to confirm this point. Archaean iron is noted for being phosphorous-free – a feature that adds to its economic value today. How, then, did some initial life-form gain access to the requisite quantities of phosphorous? The geological evidence suggests that phosphorous was only available in trace quantities, or that a most unique ancient environment existed which prevented phosphate minerals from forming. Either conclusion has a profound bearing on any discussion about the origin of life.

Reasoning of this sort, I began to see, can be extended to all the building blocks of life. How did the pure chemical compounds that build up proteins accumulate in the contamination of the Archaean era? And on and on. At some point during my stay in the northern wilderness, my sense of being troubled turned to fascination. The entire project of explaining the origin of life on conventional reductionist principles in the Archaean geological period started to seem altogether fantastic. Yet probably a majority of working scientists believe that life began spontaneously in this environment. Prior to my work as a geologist at the Joutel site, I had shared, quite uncritically, the same opinion. It was only when confronted by 'the real Archaean' that serious doubts and questions arose in my mind.

Thus began my personal search for an answer to the question of the origin of life and the mysteries of evolution that appeared to have been so securely explained by contemporary science.

At first, I was surprised to discover just how little attention the commanding heights of the scientific community still devote to the extremely troublesome questions that the contaminated environment of the very ancient Archaean era pose for the conventional wisdom of my own school-days. You can look far and wide for a demonstration or theory, or even a reference to the problem of how pure chemical species come from an impure source without ever quite finding one. The conventional wisdom still unfolds as if the origin of life took place in a protected womb rather than a turmoil of Archaean hostility. I began to suspect that much of the current debate on the subject had been 'sanitized' to accommodate an allegiance to a kind of 'Darwinian' thinking that finally reduces to its own form of blind faith.

As I carried on with my search it gradually became clear to me that science today has no explanation of how, as it were, life had come from non-life. In theory, a scientist deeply troubled by the challenges of the Archaean geological period might try to invoke some 'vital force' in nature, but no such force has ever been detected. The biogenesis principle, that only life begets life, is the deepest scientific wisdom. And this must mean that some living entity must be responsible for the origin of life.

At the end of this road I began to take seriously, in a new way, the monotheistic message I had heard before I became a geologist; that the living entity responsible for the origin of life is a living God. I was still a geologist, however, and I was still a working scientist, practising my profession. I could not help but wonder about a number of questions, that scientific habits tend to bring to mind. How could one test for the presence of a living God? What evidence would indicate 'His' presence in the affairs of nature? Did He 'create' directly, or did He use some process to bring His creation into being? If there is a living God, shouldn't we be able to understand at least a little about how this living God works?

All this has finally brought me face to face with 'evolution's hand.' And here I should quickly acknowledge that Charles Darwin was a great intellectual figure of the nineteenth century. ("What Galileo and Newton were to the seventeenth century," the British philosopher Bertrand Russell once wrote, "Darwin was to the nineteenth.")

At the same time, the concept of evolution did not start with Darwin, and it does not end with him either. Alas, while there is no such thing as Galileoism today, there still is something that might reasonably be called Darwinism. As I've already tried to explain, my own faith in this 'ism' was shaken, fundamentally and forever, on the Archaean rocks of the Canadian Shield.

In the space where my subsequent search for an answer to the origin of life and the mysteries of evolution has finally landed, two evolutionary processes have been at work in our universe. The first is responsible for the physical world as we know it, and the second for the biological world. Contemporary science has enabled us to understand a great deal about both processes, and to make human existence a much more intriguing adventure than it used to be. (Whether it will eventually make this existence more truly 'successful' is another question. I hope my work here will at least provide some food for thought).

But my ultimate contention is that if you rigorously search out what contemporary science also implies about the *origins* and *design* of both the physical and biological processes of evolution, you can (and I myself would now say can only) arrive at the presence of a living God or First Intelligence, whose living Mind has set the physical universe and all living things within it in motion. My attempt to show why and how this is so, and to answer the related questions I raised earlier, is contained in the rest of this book.

I should probably quickly acknowledge as well that before I became a geologist, I was raised as a Christian. This, no doubt, has had some impact on the way I have approached a number of the tasks which the book undertakes. In my struggles to make sense of the origin of life and the mysteries of evolution, I have also been deeply impressed by the work of the French evolutionary philosopher Lecomte du Nouy. Readers familiar with du Nouy's writing will quickly see the influence.

My own final view, however, is that the most crucial and essential core of my argument is not tied to any particular tradition of belief or philosophy, or religious or secular thought in any particular part of the world. There are many paths to apprehending the Spirit of the living God. What I have to say does not delve into any of them.

CHAPTER 1

"In the beginning ..."

Over six thousand years ago, a Middle Eastern nomad opened the most famous book of western literature (and at least one of the better-known writings of all time) with "In the beginning" – Genesis, chapter one, line one. These three simple words contain no ambiguity. If one believed that the Judaeo-Christian Bible was divinely inspired, then one had to accept that there was a beginning to the universe. Such a position caused untold intellectual grief to many believers who followed. No obvious reason existed as to why any thinking person would subscribe to the notion of any kind of beginning to our universe. A commitment to the notion of a creative act that brought the entire universe into being was an act of faith.

Classical western civilization was intellectually dominated by Greek wisdom. Even today, Socrates, Plato, and Aristotle are household names, while Euclidian geometry is still standard fare for high school mathematics courses. The wise men of Greece reflected on the nature of the universe and concluded that it was eternal – showing no sign of a beginning and no prospect of an end. Monotheistic philosophers found themselves in a difficult position. Saint Thomas Aquinas, one of Christendom's intellectual giants in the middle ages, felt forced to concede that the 'pagan' Aristotle had the better argument. Aquinas had to believe on faith what he had failed to demonstrate by logical argument – that there was a beginning to everything in the universe.

From a scientific point of view Genesis was a role of the dice, since science cannot entertain the notion of divine inspiration. The wise men of Greece had declared against the notion, but nobody really knew whether the universe had a beginning or not. It is instructive to speculate on the prognosis for monotheistic philosophy if science had actually uncovered an eternal universe in the more recent past. I'd suggest that monotheism would be in a state of complete disarray, since it would be impossible to mount an argument that such traditional writings as the book of Genesis were totally allegorical. As it happens, however, monotheistic thought has not had to deal with such a scenario.

GENESIS IN THE UNIVERSE: THE BIG BANG

Seven centuries after the time of Aquinas, and six thousand years after some Middle Eastern nomad began the book of Genesis, twentieth-century science has amassed formidable evidence of a beginning to our universe. Albert Einstein's general theory of relativity predicts such a beginning. Tragically, when Einstein first derived his general theory he could not accept its conclusion that the universe had to be expanding, and was not stationary at all. He introduced a correction factor into his equations to eliminate the expansion. It was a decision he regretted for the rest of his life, often describing it as the biggest blunder of his scientific career.

In 1929, the American astronomer Edwin Hubble confirmed that the universe really was expanding. Using the red shift of the Doppler effect, he found that all galaxies, with the exception of our 'near' neighbours, were moving away from us. Though this was amazing in its own right, Hubble also noted that the 'speed' with which our less-immediate galactic neighbours, moved away from us was proportional to their distance from our own galaxy. Thus, a galaxy four times further away was moving away four times as fast. Hubble had discovered a universe that was expanding uniformly in all directions.

It follows that if the universe is expanding at present, when we go back in time the universe must be smaller. And the further back in cosmic history one travels, the smaller the universe becomes. But this is not an infinite regression: eventually the size of the universe must reduce to a single infinitesimal point.

Einstein's theory of relativity and Hubble's astronomical observations opened the door for the so-called 'big bang' theory of the origins of our universe.[1] According to this conception, the universe started as an infinitely dense hot point at the beginning of time. The hot point is known as a singularity – a physical condition where the known laws of science break down. From this beginning, the universe has been expanding and evolving ever since.

The big bang theory predicts that there should be residual radiation left over from the beginning of the universe. This radiation would have started out at a very high temperature, but as the universe cooled down it would have been stretched out and become much colder. The American astronomer Jim Peebles calculated that the so-called "cosmic microwave radiation" left over from the big bang would have a temperature of less than 263 degrees Celsius. Then in 1964, Arno Penzias and Robert Wilson actually discovered the predicted background radiation, and helped put the big bang theory on an increasingly secure foundation.

In 1989, NASA launched its Cosmic Background Explorer (COBE) satellite. COBE confirmed the presence of microwave background radiation with certain levels of fluctuations. And these fluctuations are of the right magnitude to explain the later formation of galaxies and other large-scale structures in the universe through the influence of gravity. These findings have helped prompt almost unanimous acceptance of a big bang model for our universe's origins within the scientific community.[2] It now makes quite a lot of sense to say that the moment of the big bang was a moment in the time of our universe when there was no before.

Between 10 and 20 billion years ago all the matter, energy, space, and time of the universe were concentrated at a point into one nearly homogeneous fiery plasma, with temperatures in excess of 10 billion degrees Celsius. The big bang caused this fiery plasma to come into existence and to begin expanding. Exactly how it expanded is currently a subject of much debate. In the standard 'hot big bang' model, it expanded with absolutely precise initial conditions to evolve into the universe we know today. These initial conditions had to be so precise and finely tuned that accuracies in the range of one in sixty orders of magnitude (a number with sixty zeros) have been calculated.

Such uniquely specific initial conditions are so difficult to explain that they virtually invite the hypothesis of some form of Creator. Perhaps for this reason, physicists have lately been hard at work developing alternatives to the hot big bang. So-called 'inflation models' are the current favourites. In these models the expansion of the universe had to occur at a rate greater than that of the speed of light in the earliest fractions of time (hence the term 'inflation'). The expansion continues to this day, albeit at a slower rate. The actual expansion is in the fabric of space/time itself, and there is no question of matter and energy hurtling through pre-existing space. Thus, inflation models do not violate Einstein's general theory of relativity. At the same time, an expansion in excess of the speed of light is something of a strange concept. New space is being created or generated right to the present day.

No matter which big bang model one chooses, energy, matter, space, and the arrow of time were all born "in the beginning." As matters stand, the fundamental relationships between forces and the laws of physics were born as well. None of the laws of physics can be considered primary. Like matter, energy, and space/time, all evolved from the initial momentous event. The universe and the laws of physics that describe its workings are all derivatives of the 'initial flash' of the big bang.

CREATION AND THE BEGINNING

After the initial flash, the universe began its expansion. There are two immediately obvious and extreme ways in which the universe could expand. In the first, the expansion could be slow enough so as to allow the force of gravity to arrest it, thus causing the universe to collapse back into the fiery inferno from whence it came. Under these conditions, the universe would be a closed system. In the second, the rate of expansion could be so fast that the force of gravity would be ineffectual. The universe would go on expanding indefinitely, and there would be little chance of any galaxies and stars forming under the influence of gravity. Under these conditions, the universe would be an open system. As it happens, the universe is expanding at an exactly balanced rate between these two extremes, and it is difficult to say whether the universe is open or closed.

It is this razor-edged balance of forces that allows the universe to evolve in the complex manner that it has. When physicists extrapolate back to the big bang, they conclude that this balance between the force of gravity and the rate of expansion was absolutely perfect. So Stephen Hawking remarks in relation to the hot big bang model:

> This means that the initial state of the universe must have been very carefully chosen indeed, if the hot big bang model was correct right back to the beginning of time. It would be very difficult to explain why the universe should have begun in just this way, except as the act of a God who intended to create beings like us.[3]

It is imprudent in the extreme to build castles on the shifting sands of the frontiers of science. It does seem that since the hot big bang model of the beginning of the universe almost demands a 'Creator,' science has sought out alternative models. In my opinion this is an entirely legitimate exercise. Science ought to exhaust all possibilities, other than a Creator, to explain "the difficulty of the day." If science does not carry out its duty in this respect, all we will be left with is a god of the gaps instead of a Creator. And this scenario ought to be unacceptable to all concerned.

Inflationary big bang models have been proposed so as to account for the seemingly perfect balance between the force of gravity and the expansion of the universe. As already noted, these models require a rate of expansion in excess of the speed of light in the earliest fractions of a second in the history of the universe. Rather than explaining the initial conditions of the universe, a model of this sort erases any evidence of them by smoothing out any initial irregularities. An inflationary model appears to allow a far wider range of initial conditions than the hot big bang model, and this in turn reduces the need for perfect balance in the expansion of the universe and gravity. NASA's COBE satellite results, mentioned above, are often thought to give considerable credence to the inflation hypothesis.[4]

If inflation models of the beginning of the universe have lately been gaining strength, however, their scientific foundation remains somewhat insecure. It also remains to be seen just how much of a cosmic coincidence inflation, itself, represents. How much leeway exists, for example, in the duration of the inflationary phase? If the inflationary phase did not last long enough, would the universe have collapsed back into itself through the force of gravity? Moreover, while inflation models may help explain the seemingly precise balance between the rate of expansion of the universe and the force of gravity, and thus eliminate some immediate call for a Creator, they still do quite a lot to reinforce the claims of monotheistic philosophy.

Traditionally, many monotheists have advocated creation *ex nihilo* or out of nothing. The mechanics of such a proposition have been, to put it mildly, difficult to envision. For centuries monotheism has struggled in vain to offer a rational explanation of how something real like a universe can come out of nothing. Now the quantum mechanics involved in the inflation model of the big bang may point the way forward.

The inflationary big bang theory of the origin of the universe presents a strange scenario for contemporary science. Ultimately, science may have to face the possibility that our entire universe arose from a quantum fluctuation in a vacuum – or, in simper language, from nothing at all. Hawking quotes Alan Guth, the father of inflationary big bang theory: "It is said that there is no such thing as a free lunch. But the universe is the ultimate free lunch."[5]

What Guth means is that the universe is composed of positive and negative energy. Gravity is negative energy and everything else is positive. The universe exists because the positive and negative energies have been separated by the big bang. When they are brought back together they will cancel each other out exactly. If ever science were to come up with a theory compatible with monotheistic thinking, this must be it. Creation has been the cornerstone of monotheistic thought for thousands of years. Now scientists are not just asserting that it is a real possibility: they are also constructing models to explain how it might have taken place. It is now a reasonable enough proposition that real things like our universe can come from nothing at all. And it remains quite difficult to conceive how any quantum fluctuation of the magnitude of the big bang could have come about by "its own" volition.

THE EVOLVING UNIVERSE AND COSMIC COINCIDENCES

If the big bang that began the universe has opened up some provocative new room for an act of creation, the subsequent evolution of what the big bang began has also raised some provocative prospects of particular creative acts of design.

To start with, the universe is a different place today than it was during the early moments of the big bang. It exists in a perpetual state of dynamic flux – forever changing and evolving. Most of the stars examined by astronomers contain heavy elements, from which we can conclude that they belong to at least a second generation of their type. The bulk of first-generation stars are extinct, some of them having exploded as supernovas, showering heavy elements into space. These heavy elements were later incorporated into the second-generation stars of the present, which emit tell-tale, heavy-element spectra detectable here on Earth.

We can make these assertions because the laws of physics have been found to have universal application. As physicists have attempted to reconstruct the history of the universe, they have not hit dead ends, demanding new laws to explain their observations. Our understanding of the laws of physics has been gained by observation and experiment here on our small planet. It is a singular result that these laws are found to be faithful throughout the universe. Why this should be so is one of the great mysteries of science. And one can reasonably enough pose the question of whether there is some underlying form of fundamental logic or deliberate design in how the universe works.

Thus, we now accept the idea that change is the normal state of affairs for the universe. Virtually nothing stays the same, with the great exception of the laws of physics. The universe is driven to change or evolve by its intrinsic characteristics. The big bang was the impetus, and the controlling parameters are the laws of physics. Essentially, science has discovered a universe uniquely receptive to complex life, through a veritable tailor-made set of laws and relationships. In science today these laws and relationships give rise to a variety of so-called 'cosmic coincidences,' and these coincidences carry their own implications of some form of intelligent design (or even some intelligent 'Designer') at work.[6]

THE CRUCIAL CASE OF DEUTERIUM

Everything in the universe is a derivative of whatever precipitated the big bang. This includes all the energy, matter, space/time, and the laws of physics. Science has found that many of the fundamental relationships and constants of physics are precisely and delicately attuned to each other. These precise balances allow the universe to evolve into a state of maximum physical complexity. And from this one might reasonably argue that the universe was deliberately designed to evolve in such a way as to create a hospitable environment for complex, conscious observers such as humankind.

With the exception of the actual beginning itself, which must forever remain undefined, physicists today are confident that they can reconstruct most of the first three minutes of the big bang. In the first fraction of a second the universe started out as a seething froth of elementary particles at extreme temperatures. Neutrons and protons, the essential building blocks of matter, played only a small role in this initial broth. Then, as the temperature fell with the expansion of the universe, neutrons started to decay into protons by a radioactive process known as beta decay, whereby neutrons emit electrons and neutrinos and turn into protons.

Before all the neutrons could decay into protons, another process fortuitously came into play. This is the nuclear fusion of neutrons and protons into the hydrogen isotope, deuterium. Deuterium was unstable at the higher temperatures of the big bang, but it became stable before all the neutrons could decay. Once the neutrons were bound in the nucleus of deuterium they were stable. Thus the existence of neutrons depended on the stability temperature of deuterium being what it is. If the stability temperature of deuterium had been somewhat lower than it is, most of the neutrons in the universe would have decayed into protons, and little or no deuterium would have formed.

Deuterium is important because it is an essential building block in the synthesis of all elements heavier than hydrogen. Heavy elements are formed within large dying stars by the process of nuclear fusion or nucleosynthesis. Most of these heavier elements are far more stable than deuterium itself. Hence, the world as we know it was able to evolve into a state based on the arbitrary stability of deuterium. Had the stability temperature been a little lower, our universe would have been stillborn. And this raises the quite provocative question of why deuterium should have had just the right stability temperature.

OTHER COSMIC COINCIDENCES

In fact the stability of deuterium depends on the nuclear force[7] – the same force involved in nuclear explosions. If this force had been set a little higher, then all the hydrogen in the universe would have been converted to deuterium and then to helium, and no stars at all would have existed. And, as already noted, if it had been a little weaker heavy elements could never have formed. Why the nuclear force has the value it does, science cannot answer, but it was obliged to have this value if the universe was to evolve elemental complexity. If this were the only coincidence, then it would only be a curiosity. Yet science has uncovered a whole suite of such coincidences and finely tuned balancing relationships.

No theory exists which allows scientists to predict the values of the fundamental forces in nature. One is thus left with the conclusion that they could have assumed a great range of values. The evolution of the universe, however, provides no latitude: the values of the forces must be exactly what they are, or the universe and we who live within it could not exist.

The gravitational force is 38 orders of magnitude less powerful than the electrical force that controls the strength of chemical bonds. We can argue that this weakness in the gravitational force allows for great lengths of time and thus allows for the greatest possible complexity in physical evolution. Every star exists in a state of conflict between the ordinary electrical forces of atoms and molecules, and the gravitational force of its mass.

Gravity tends to crush the star out of existence, while the electrical forces of the atoms resist the pressure. If the force of gravity had been a little stronger, additional smaller stars would have formed, and they would have been short-lived and ineffectual generators of heat. Any larger stars would have burned out much more quickly. If the force had been a little weaker, stars would not have formed at all because the gravitational force could not have pulled clouds of gases together to form galaxies and stars. The force of gravity is as weak as it possibly can be to accommodate long-lasting stars. It is in this sense that one can say the force of gravity has been 'set' to maximize the length of time in the universe. And this, in turn, allows the maximum amount of time for complexity to evolve.

To take the argument another step again, four fundamental forces exist in the universe: the force of gravity, the nuclear force, the strong electrical force, and the weak electrical force. The ability of the universe to evolve physically depends on the precise relationships of these forces to each other. Science has determined that the actual values of these forces maximize the universe's potential for complex physical evolution. No latitude in these values appears possible. Even minor deviations would precipitate a far simpler universe, in which no complex life-forms, such as human beings, could exist.

This predisposition to complex evolutionary patterns is particularly striking in the formation of the heavy elements. In the nuclear synthesis of the elements hydrogen fuses to form helium, and then helium in turn fuses to form beryllium. But the beryllium thus formed is so unstable that it can exist for only a fraction of a second. By right this instability of beryllium should have put an end to the further synthesis of the elements. But it just happens that the next element in the sequence, carbon, has a natural energy level that favours, through what is known as resonance, the synthesis of beryllium and helium. Thus, although beryllium is a highly unstable element, the synthesis of carbon is permitted.

The next element in the sequence should be oxygen, and so on until iron is reached. Yet if this sequence were followed, there would be no chemical diversity at all, and the universe would be a very uninteresting iron-rich place, with no potential for housing complex creatures such as ourselves. Fortunately, the natural energy levels in oxygen inhibit the synthesis of carbon and helium. If the critical energy level in carbon had been lower by a few percentage points, no heavy elements could have formed. At the same time, if the critical energy level in oxygen had been a few percentage points higher, then iron would have been the only heavy element that could form. Again, the complexity of our universe depends on some very finely tuned counterbalances in fundamental physical relationships – all derived in the cosmic beginning at the time of the big bang.

A FINAL CASE: THE WONDERFUL
WORLD OF WATER ON EARTH

Another striking and coincidental feature of the particular situation on our own small planet involves the vital properties of certain elements under the moderate conditions found at the Earth's surface – considering that all these elements were forged in extreme conditions in the cores of giant stars, at unthinkable pressures and millions of degrees Celsius.

Life as we know it is a carbon/water-based system. Carbon has an uncanny ability to form giant molecules, known as polymers, and this property is indispensable to life. At the same time, it was not present under the extreme conditions in which carbon was synthesized originally. Water is the molecule formed by the union of two hydrogen atoms and one oxygen atom. It is the fundamental source of hydrogen for the crucial energy process of life known as photosynthesis. It is also one of the finest solvents known to chemistry, and it facilitates all sorts of wonderful chemical reactions. The chemistry of life depends on the proteins known as enzymes, and enzymes all work in the medium of water.

So water plays a vital physical role in promoting life on Earth. It also has the very unique property that it is at its most dense at four degrees Celsius. This allows its solid form, ice, to float in its liquid form. And this unique property allows the Earth to have large quantities of water without freezing over. It is not hard to imagine what would happen if ice sank in liquid water. The geological record testifies to many ice ages during the Earth's history, and this is easy enough to understand. Maintaining the long-range temperature of the Earth between zero and 100 degrees Celsius is a delicate balancing operation in its own right.

If ice were capable of sinking during an ice age, then all the ice formed in the polar regions of the Earth would sink to the bottom of the sea. In a very short time an impenetrable barrier of ice would build up, and this would effectively block the hot currents from the equator. Without any heat arriving from the equator, the ice would be free to continue building up. As it did so the Earth would continuously lose solar heat, due to the reflective properties of ice (the so-called albedo effect). This, in turn, would promote the formation of more ice until even the equator was frozen over, and no water-based life system could flourish. Yet again, the right properties just seem to have come into being, even though their origins lie in the unthinkable extremes of the big bang and the cores of large stars.

No matter how one looks at it, in order for humanity to exist at all our universe must be exactly the way it is. Even our three-dimensional space is an essential component. No planetary orbit could be stable in a space composed of more than three dimensions, because the planetary orbits would decay rapidly and the planet would plunge into the sun. Yet there is no compelling reason whatsoever that space should be composed of just three dimensions. Particle physicists are happily talking about a world with many more.

As best as I can tell, cosmic coincidences of this sort have as yet made very little impression on popular thought today, and this surprises me somewhat. They are well-known to the scientific community, and they are discussed in a number of ostensibly popular scientific books. I have only taken time to touch on the subject quickly here. Combining all the 'coincidences' we know about now, however, raises some rather impressive evidence for the intelligent design of our universe. As Hawking has remarked:

> Nevertheless, it seems clear that there are relatively few ranges of values for the numbers that would allow the development of any form of intelligent life. Most sets of values would give rise to universes that, although they might be very beautiful, would contain no one able to wonder at that beauty. One can take this either as evidence of a divine purpose in Creation and the choice of the laws of science or as support for the strong anthropic principle.[8]

Cosmic coincidences in this sense present certain earlier conceptions of what 'science' is all about with some new problems. As science has taught, the universe is in process and it must evolve. But the reason it must evolve is what causes all the problems. It is the exquisite balance in the fundamental forces of nature that drives the physical evolution of our universe. And this balance has at least every appearance of some form of purpose. There exist a near infinite number of potential combinations of the fundamental forces of nature that would collectively produce nothing of interest at all.

PURPOSEFUL EVOLUTION IN A
COMPREHENSIBLE UNIVERSE

Of course a purposeful universe is exactly what traditional monotheistic thought about 'creation' would predict. The Creator is not capricious: the universe will evolve according to a plan. The perfect balances in the fundamental forces of nature are simply a means to an end. They secure the evolution of a complex universe. There was a beginning to our universe, and from this beginning it is evolving in accordance with a 'master plan.' What happened was supposed to happen. 'Chance' only plays a role at the local level.

In this same spirit, my argument is that our current knowledge of the physical evolution of the universe allows us to suggest what might be called a monotheistic model of evolution, where evolution is conceived as the tool of a Creator, that produces purposeful results. This model has several hallmarks. (1) The evolutionary process starts out as a singularity or a discontinuity. We cannot explain the conditions after the singularity by means of the conditions prior to the singularity. (2) The process has an ability to generate ever more complex structures from simpler structures. (3) Purpose pervades the major features of the process and its structures. (4) There exist unique sets of initial values, so that the evolutionary process will unfold, but within the preset structures great freedom is permitted and chance generates variety rather than complexity at the local level. (5) Though science abhors singularities, I am proposing that two exist: one for the physical origin of the universe and one for the biological origin of life. The Creator, as it were, used one form of evolution to bring the physical world into being (as I have been discussing in this chapter), and another for the biological world (as I will discuss in later parts of the book).

Proceeding down this road, it takes all of the universe's evolutionary prowess to furnish an environment capable of sustaining complex creatures such as humanity. 'We' must be seen as one of the universe's most complex evolutionary achievements, since it takes all the properties and the vastness of energy, matter, space, and time to allow our existence in the first place. In the universe humanity is a local maximum of complexity in the evolutionary process (and perhaps considerably more than local).

This brings us face to face with what seems to me the greatest philosophical problem confronting contemporary science. It is in the nature of the universe to evolve and we human beings, the product of evolution, are here to observe and query the whole process. Neither the universe nor ourselves are primary. We are both derivatives of evolutionary processes. We are faced with an unknowing universe generating a knowing observer.

For centuries the universe presented scientists with a multitude of riddles to be deciphered, piece by painstaking piece. Now, we have been so successful (in one sense of the word at least) in the scientific enterprise that an entirely new conundrum has emerged. The great mystery is no longer how to explain the universe, but how to explain why we are capable of explaining the universe. Why does science work and, more to the point, why has contemporary science been so spectacularly successful? Science explains the workings of the universe with tools of pure abstraction, mathematics, logic, beauty and symmetry, and scientific concepts. It has become clear that the abstractions of the human mind can penetrate the essence of the cosmos. Yet why the principles of mathematical abstraction should have any relevance at all to the universe at large remains mysterious.

Science offers no simple explanation for this intriguing puzzle. If our intelligence can penetrate the workings of the universe, then it seems only reasonable to posit the existence of some Primary Intelligence responsible for these same workings. Again, the monotheistic philosopher could hardly be more comfortable. The intelligence we are invited to posit is that of the Creator. The alternative is to accept an intelligible universe without an intelligent Creator. And on this scenario one also has to accept that intelligence arose from nothing.

As it happens, contemporary scientists have themselves been puzzling over why their enterprise works in the first place. So Stephen Hawking has written:

> What is it that breathes fire into the equations and makes a universe for them to describe? The usual approach of science of constructing a mathematical model cannot answer questions of why there should be a universe for the model to describe.[9]

According to A.R. Peacocke:

> The realization that our minds can find the world intelligible, and the implications this has that an explanation for the world process is to be found in mental rather than purely material categories, has been for many scientists who are theists, including the present writer, an essential turning-point in their thinking. Why should science work at all? That it does so points strongly to a principle of rationality, to an interpretation of the cosmos in terms of mind as its

most significant feature. ... There is clearly a kinship between the mind of man and the cosmos which is real, and which any account of the cosmos cannot ignore.[10]

According to Einstein:

> It seems the human mind has first to construct forms independently before we can find them in things. Kepler's marvellous achievement is a particularly fine example of the truth that knowledge cannot spring from experience alone but only from the comparison of the inventions of the intellect with observed fact.[11]

And, finally, Michael Talbot has quite provocatively written:

> No scientist working today can deny that aesthetics, something that is purely a product of the inward reality of our consciousness, also provides us with a map for discovering the outward reality of the universe. But why is this so? ... Or as Yale biophysicist Harold Morowitz has put it, why is it, when we work through Newton's second law of motion for the first time, we get "the feeling of a return to some primordial knowledge?"... As Einstein wrote in 1921, "Here arises a puzzle that has disturbed scientists of all periods. How is it possible that mathematics, a product of human thought that is independent of experience, fits so excellently the objects of physical reality? Can human reason without experience discover by pure thinking the properties of real things?" ... Wigner concluded that the structure of mathematics and the structure of the physical universe are disturbingly similar. Wigner capped off his paper with a quote from the late philosopher Charles Peirce "that there is some secret here which remains to be discovered."[12]

I agree myself: something does remain to be discovered. Above all it is the two-way flow between human intelligence and the universe that inspires the scientific imagination. If human intelligence confronted an unintelligible universe, then we could accept our intelligence as some mere local phenomenon. When we find that our intelligence can help unlock the greater universe, something of greater import is implied. Physicists have to account for this compatibility of the human mind with their theory of how the universe began. If the origin of the universe in a quantum fluctuation were just a chance event, then how could we know it happened? For me this compatibility of the human mind with the universe at large is the strongest argument for the existence of a Creator. We can track down the Creator through the trail of His intelligence, as it is revealed to human intelligence in His Creation. Tracking down the beginning of the universe, and its purposeful evolution, has been our first step.

THE NEXT STEP AHEAD

In summing-up the arguments of this chapter, we could say that theological predictions of a beginning no longer conflict with the outlook of contemporary science and the habits of ordinary thinking people – as they once did for Saint Thomas Aquinas, pondering the pagan thoughts of Aristotle. The 'big bang' has every appearance of what one would anticipate an act of creation would be.

Reinforcing the monotheistic position is the extraordinary balance of forces that drive the physical evolution of the universe. The universe must evolve, but only because a highly improbable balance of forces makes it evolve. Monotheists must of course accept the 'use' of evolution by a Creator. And we have in the evolutionary history of the universe a model of how a Creator can use evolution to achieve complexity, purpose, and design.

Above all else, science has uncovered an astonishing compatibility between the human mind and the universe at large. Human abstractions such as symmetry, beauty, and mathematics are pivotal in explaining the workings of the universe. These are the qualities of intelligence. It takes an intelligence to comprehend Intelligence, and there are good reasons to argue that the universe has been intelligently designed. The First Intelligence belongs to the Creator. And we can use human intelligence to search for the Creator's living Mind.

The scientific evidence is compatible with the hypothesis that the physical universe is designed to evolve in a purposeful manner. If physical evolution implies purpose, then biological evolution should imply purpose as well. If physical evolution suggests powerful evidence for the existence of a Creator, then biological evolution should do the same. Human intelligence is the child of biological evolution. And this binds the evolutionary process and human intelligence together. If it takes intelligence to comprehend Intelligence, then it is reasonable enough to hypothesize that it takes Intelligence to beget intelligence. Exploring the origin of human intelligence is the next step in the search.

1 As a term depicting the beginning of our universe, 'big bang' leaves a lot to be desired. It was originally coined by Fred Hoyle as a term of derision, and subsequently taken up as an at least memorable catch-phrase for a somewhat complicated theory. In the end, the catch-phrase stuck.

2. A number of different specific big bang models have been proposed, and there is a scientific growth industry in the area of cosmology. Some examples of readily available books that interested readers might consult include: J. Barrow and F. Tippler, *The Anthropic Cosmological Principle* (Oxford: Oxford University Press, 1986); P. Davies, *The Cosmic Blueprint* (New York: Simon and Shuster, 1989), *The Mind of God* (New York: Simon and Shuster, 1991), and *The Last Three Minutes* (New York: Basic Books, 1994); J. Gribbin and M. Rees, *Cosmic Coincidences: Dark Matter, Mankind, and Anthropic Cosmology* (New York: Bantam Books, 1989); S. Hawking, *A Brief History Of Time* (London: Bantam Books, 1988) and *Black Holes and Baby Universes and Other Essays* (London: Bantam Books, 1993); P. Halpern, *The Cyclical Serpent: Prospects for an Ever-Repeating Universe* (New York: Plenum Press, 1995); and S. Weinberg, *The First Three Minutes: A Modern View of the Origin of the Universe* (New York: Basic Books, 1988). This list is by no means exhaustive. What all these books suggest is that the big bang model of the universe's origins now rests on rather secure scientific foundations. Beyond this, one enters much more speculative ground. Cosmology is a subject still in its infancy.

3 Hawking, *Brief History of Time*, 127. A note of caution is probably in order. One of the most obscure aspects of Hawking's writing involves his references to God. These often seem to mean rather different and frequently unconventional things, though here he does appear to be referring to God in the traditional sense of a supreme creative Being.

4 See J. Gribbon, *In The Beginning: After COBE and Before the Big Bang* (Boston: Little, Brown and Company, 1993). Gribbon offers a highly readable account of the discovery and significance of the fluctuations in the cosmic microwave radiation in his early chapters.

5 Hawking, *Brief History of Time*, 129.

6 These coincidences in the fundamental numbers of science can be found in detail in Barrow and Tippler, *Anthropic Cosmological Principle*. The authors offer three possible explanations for the strong anthropic principle, one of which is the deliberate action of a Designer. To my mind, cosmic coincidences represent some of the most fertile ground in the search for evidence of a Creator. Alas, they are still not well-known or appreciated by the general public. Physicists cannot be blamed, since many of the popular books on cosmology do deal with the subject. Perhaps it is just that these books are not yet as widely read as they might be, and that there is still much to be done in the mission of popular scientific education.

7 The nuclear force is usually referred to as the strong force.

8 Hawking, *Brief History of Time*, 125.

9 Ibid., 174.

10 A.R. Peacocke, *Science and the Christian Experiment* (Oxford: Oxford University Press, 1971), 133.

11 A. Einstein, *Ideas and Opinions* (New York: Crown Trade Paperbacks, 1982), 266.

12 M. Talbot, *Beyond the Quantum* (New York: Macmillan Publishing Company, 1986), 190.

CHAPTER 2

The Awakening: The Emergence of Human Intelligence

Unlike others in the animal kingdom, he stands upright on his two hind limbs. In this posture he measures just under six feet tall and weighs over 150 pounds. She stands just over five feet tall and weighs 100 odd pounds.

Physically they are the least endowed predators of all. Their teeth are puny and they wouldn't dare get into a biting competition with any self-respecting pint-sized monkey. Their nails are so inoffensive as claws that they can barely scrape themselves. They can claim to outpace the tortoise but few other animals. They can climb, but among the tree dwellers they are poor competitors. They can swim, but in the water they are neither swift nor agile. Their noses have less than one percent the sensitivity of a dog's and their hearing is not much better. They stand on the face of the Earth completely naked. They are at the mercy of the elements: exposed, they can freeze to death or burn in the sun. Compared with any other animal the child at their side is helpless and dependent for an inordinate length of time. In giving birth she enters into an agonizing game of Russian roulette.

Predators, whether they be hawks or vipers, great cats or white sharks, or even the now legendary Tyrannosaurus Rex, have all been physically fearsome creatures. In this light it is surprising that this fragile pair not only rank among the most dominant of predators, but surpass in power all who have ever reigned on Earth. Unlike all their ruling predecessors, their dominion derives not from their great animal strength but from the very absence of strength.

This pair has rewritten the rules of engagement in the animal world and introduced a completely novel paradigm for life. All the weapons historically associated with the top carnivore have been swapped for a large neural muscle in their head. Their brain is not just their weapon of choice; it is the only real weapon they have – the physical machine that has allowed them to switch from animal instinct to learning. With the brain's innate prowess for learning, logical manipulation of knowledge has become their fearful claw and deadly incisor. How did this pair come to possess such a lethal instrument?

EXPLAINING THE EVOLUTION OF LARGER BRAINS

Vertebrates are the brainiest and the most complex of all animals. Human beings belong to the vertebrate class known as mammals. The ancestors of the mammals came from the reptile class, and the reptiles in turn evolved from the amphibian class, who in turn came from the class of fish. Each class of vertebrate is composed of conscious creatures who react to a variable range of stimuli from their environment.

When we examine the general brain development of these four vertebrate classes, linked by their evolutionary history, a very strong pattern immediately emerges. If we compare the ratio of brain weight to the two-thirds power of body weight in vertebrates we have an excellent measure of relative brain size.[1] Using this measure we can group the fish, amphibians, and the reptiles into a large group known as the lower vertebrates. The fish have consistently the least brain development. The amphibians and the reptiles have generally more brain development but they are still relatively close to the fish. The first mammals to evolve, the ancient mammals, have more brain development than any reptile or amphibian. The modern mammals in turn have far more brain development than the ancient mammals. The evolutionary succession from fish to modern mammals has generated progressive increments in brain size. These four ancestrally linked classes of vertebrate exhibit an evolutionary trend of increasing brain size.

The increasing 'braininess' or encephalization of the vertebrates as shown by the evolutionary history of these organisms is one of the most important trends in all of evolution. It crosses four classes and it is clearly and unambiguously progressive. One cannot look at a graph of this increase in brain size without seeing the trend.[2]

When a trend is discovered in nature the scientist has the scent of some cause and effect relationship at work. Invariably there is some factor responsible for the existence of the trend. In the final analysis one wants to determine whether the trend is fully explained by known natural causes, or whether there is an unknown factor at work. In the case at hand we want to determine whether contingent genetic mutations acted upon by natural selection can fully explain the increasing brain size, or whether we should look for some directing property underlying the evolutionary process. Whatever viewpoint the reader is predisposed to, there *is* an evolutionary trend of increasing brain size. And it demands some explanation.

THE PRIMATES

Humanity belongs to the primate order, which includes approximately 200 species among the lemurs, monkeys, great apes, and the hominids.[3] The earlier history of the primates is dominated by a tree-dwelling way of life. The actual fossil evidence for primate history is quite poor, because tree-dwelling animals leave few fossils. To be preserved as a fossil an animal carcass has to have a good chance of being buried quickly, and tree-dwelling reduces the probability of preservation drastically. Hence primates have a scanty fossil record. And a great deal of sometimes contentious inference is required in exploring their history.

The primates diverge first, in the form of the lemurs, from tree-dwelling and insect-eating ancestors. The lemur is a vegetarian and has binocular vision without any colour discrimination. Most lemurs have a reflective layer of tissue behind the retina that indicates a nocturnal way of life, or a close ancestor that was nocturnal. The lemurs have and use a highly developed sense of smell, and they are prone to using sound a lot in social groups or 'troops.' The group known as the tarsioids, represented today by tarsius in the East Indies, is believed to represent a stage of development between the lemurs and the monkeys. Tarsius is quite evolved and unlikely to be representative of ancestral tarsioids.

Next the monkeys develop. The world of the monkeys is dominated by sight. The monkeys have also continued the trend of the lemurs in using sound as a means of communication, and living within more complex social systems. There are two groups of monkeys: those of South America or the new world, and those of Africa and other parts of the old world. And it is the old-world monkeys who ultimately gave rise to the human line. The trend in the old-world line of primates is for greater increase in size, and for the primates to come down from the trees. From the monkey on, the primates have the capacity to focus sight clearly on objects because of a special adaptation in the centre of the retina called the *fovea centralis*, which permits the visual resolution of fine detail. (This feature has also developed in the present tarsius, but not to the same degree as in monkeys.)

What is most critical for our discussion here is that monkeys also have much-enlarged brains. The macaque monkeys are clearly able to learn from their environment and to learn socially. Experiments have shown that an adaptation learned by one member of the group can be learned in turn by others. In Japan the macaques gradually developed the habit of taking hot baths in volcanic springs. This implication that they can learn from each other has been independently verified by other experiments and observations. Monkeys also have the habit of sitting upright – a precursor to bipedalism. And they display notable advances in social complexity. The monkey is insatiably curious as well. His excellent eyesight and relatively dextrous and free hands allow him to reach out and touch what he sees. Curiosity, in fact, is a marked feature of all later-evolved primates.

From the monkey line come the apes, who accentuate the characteristics of the monkeys. Their brain is larger again. They have more complex social structures, and they continue the trend to partial bipedalism – swinging from branch to branch in an upright posture, occasionally running on two legs, and sitting upright. Within the apes the gibbons were first to split off the hominid line. They have become masterful acrobats, live in tight communities, and are renowned for making a lot of noise. After the gibbons the orangutan split off from the hominid line. The orangutans tend to be less sociable than other primates. Often the male lives a solitary life, and the female tends to keep to herself with her young. Young orangutans tend to pair off. The decline in sociability is probably due to a scattered food supply, forcing the orangutan to forage widely. Orangutans do not make a lot of noise themselves, but their vocal apparatus may indicate that their ancestors were quite noisy.

Much later, the gorilla split off the hominid line. Gorillas spend most of their time on the ground and climb awkwardly by primate standards. They also have notably restricted diets. Because of their size they do not need to fear enemies. Although they possess the largest brains in the ape world, gorillas are not the most mentally active apes. (That distinction belongs to the chimpanzees.) The gorilla's social structures are advanced but they do not reach the level of the chimp. In captivity gorillas are, nonetheless, known to perform advanced problem-solving and to exhibit high levels of mental acuity.

Finally, about 5 million years ago, the chimpanzee separated from the hominid line. Chimpanzees are much more mentally active than gorillas, and they live in large social groups of as many as 50 individuals. Their diet is very wide and they will eat meat when they get the chance. The infant-mother bond is particularly strong: young chimpanzees stay attached to their mother for about five years. This long dependency of the young is a trait strongly shared with humanity, enabling the young of both groups to be socialized. Chimpanzees have complex social structures, and practise such activities as grooming widely and frequently.

Chimpanzees' intellectual abilities (like those of gorillas, for that matter) vastly exceed the demands of their subsistence existence. Chimps in the field are capable of peeling a stick to push into termite mounds, in order to pick up termites to eat. Sticks are also used for extracting honey from beehives. Small sticks are often used to pick out marrow from bones. They use bunched-up leaves as sponges to drink from as well. They have been known to use sticks as levers, and they often use sticks or clubs in threatening gestures. Chimps have been found to organize themselves into hunting parties. Pygmy chimps are known to crack open nuts with pieces of wood: they even carry wood pieces into trees to crack nuts. All this amounts to nothing less than toolmaking, and in close study chimps have proved able to solve problems at a quite advanced level. Some pygmy chimpanzees are even semi-bipedal.[4]

To some extent, one can argue that the chimpanzee requires his intellectual ability in order to function in a complex social setting. Because he has a complex social structure the chimp requires high intelligence levels. Yet it is equally plausible that because he has high levels of intelligence he has a complex social structure. All the present research would seem to indicate that chimps can be induced to achieve much higher levels of intellectual output than is generally normal in their natural habitat. And this in turn implies that they have bigger and more intellectually powerful brains than they require for their ordinary stations in life.

The difficulty of explaining this excess intellectual capacity through the mechanism of natural selection, which lies at the heart of traditional Darwinist evolutionary theory, seems obvious enough. A big brain is a highly complex organ, and immensely expensive to run in terms of energy. Why would natural selection select a brain size so large and complex that it is never at all utilized to its full capacity?

To me this points to a notable inconsistency in the interpretation of evolution by natural selection and 'contingent mutations.' As I was taught in school, all the exquisite engineering feats of evolution are accounted for by natural selection. The vertebrate eye, the bat's sonar, and the bird's feather are practically perfect adaptations, and they are generally explained by economy. The organisms with the slight edge on efficiency will produce more offspring, and thus over time the efficiency becomes part of the genetic repertoire of the species. Yet we cannot really make much of a case for the relatively enormous brainpower of the gorilla and the chimpanzee in this context. It has not allowed them to dominate the primate world: they are successful primates but not predominantly so. In fact, generating excess brainpower that is expensive in energy to run is not economical at all. But it did happen.

The anomalous lack of evolutionary economy in the development of large brains becomes even more critical when we examine the history of the so-called hominids themselves. The general trend until the emergence of the hominids is for an increase in body size, a decline in the importance of smell, an increased importance of sight with the development of binocular vision (along with colour vision), the tendency for an upright posture in some part of the animal's life style (which also increases the coordination of hand and eye movements), a growth in curiosity, a steady increase in brain size, and an increase in the social complexity of the animal. The history of primate brain development, however, confronts us with an evolutionary trend within a trend. The entire mammalian class has evolved so as to produce larger brains than any other animals of history. The entire trend in the primates has been to produce larger brains than any other mammals of history. The average rate of brain-size increase is more pronounced in the primates than in the mammals. The evolutionary trend to greater brain size has been accelerated in the primate order. And a provocative pattern in the evolutionary development of the brain has begun to emerge.

THE DISAPPEARING TAIL

Before taking up the story of brain development in the hominids, a short digression is in order. Nearly all mammals have an active and useful appendage in their tail. The earliest members of the primate order had the same anatomical feature: both the lemurs and the monkeys have very long tails. A feature of primate evolutionary history is how anatomically conservative the process has been. There is very little difference in anatomical layout from a monkey to a chimpanzee or a human being. Often these similarities are offered as contributory evidence for the validity of biological evolution.

In fact, the monkey has all the essential anatomical features of a chimpanzee and a human being in place. But with the emergence of the great apes and the hominids, the conservation of the primate body-plan is broken into two distinctive areas. There has been a radical increase in brain size and a disappearance of the tail. The increase in brain size follows the evolutionary trend, but the disappearance of the tail does not fit any pattern as yet. Given that virtually the entire mammalian class possesses a tail, that the earliest members of the primate order had long and useful tails, and that the anatomical evolution of the primates is highly conservative, how does one account for the sudden disappearance of the tail?

Once the primates were on the ground, their tails began to reduce rather quickly. Baboons walk around with their tail bent at the halfway mark, and they put it to little use. The drill and mandrill have short little stumps. The gorilla, the chimpanzee, and humans have no tail at all. Yet it is not obvious why the primate tail should disappear so completely when the creature is on the ground. Vestigial organs are the stuff of evolution, and a vestigial tail should be conspicuous. Whales have retained hair on their noses and teeth that do not erupt. Pythons have retained a rudimentary hind limb structure that has not been used for a great length of time. And flightless birds still retain their wings. In human embryology a rudimentary bulge occurs where one would expect to find the tail developing, but this bulge is reabsorbed quickly. All vestiges of the tail have been eliminated. It is not just a matter of the tail not developing: the genetic information about this appendage has disappeared altogether.

The principles of natural selection suggest the argument that having a tail was a major disadvantage for the ground-dwelling primates, and so was selected out of the population. It is closer to the truth to say that it was eradicated rather ruthlessly in what is a very short span of evolutionary time. What conceivable disadvantage could a vestigial tail have been to some primates and not others? The baboons have been a very successful group. No matter what way one looks at it, having a small tail can hardly be a matter of life and death.

On the other hand, the monkeys of the new world present a somewhat different evolutionary puzzle. How is it that they never evolved into apes or something similar? The development of intelligence in the South American monkeys came to a complete standstill for a great length of time. But many of the South American monkeys did develop their tail into a prehensile fifth limb. (And some monkeys in the Philippines appear to have developed a similar form of tail.) The end of this tail has no hair on the inside, exposing skin that can grip a branch firmly. Allied to this is a whole suite of muscles that have been developed to work the tail. Monkeys in both the old and new worlds continuously use their tail for fine balancing actions. This suggests some correlation between intelligence and the presence of a tail. When the tail is put to continuous use, and in many cases developed into a fifth limb, no extra intelligence is evolved. When the tail is reduced the primates have descended to the ground, and have begun the rapid development of intelligence.

We can correlate brain development with the loss of a tail, in other words, and it would appear to be a most arbitrary correlation indeed. Is this natural selection or 'design' at work? One obvious use of the tail on bipedal dinosaurs was to maintain balance, and monkeys employ their tail for balance as well. In humankind the balancing controls are in the ear – and 'wired' to the brain. In this sense the brain can substitute for a tail. But that does not explain why even a vestige of a tail in an anatomically conservative group does not remain. What explanation can the principles of natural selection provide?

Mammals with tails and in particular the early primates are far too successful to argue for some lethal disadvantage in having a tail. That the human being has not even a vestige of a tail means that the entire genetic information for a tail has been eliminated. This implies that there had to be a mutation removing this information. It also implies that removing even a vestige of the tail presented the mutant with some great advantage. What can the advantage have been? The ancestral tail-less mutant had to dominate the reproductive process through some sort of selection, but there exists no conceivable selective force that would eliminate the tail right down to the genetic information.

My own view is that the disappearance of the tail anticipates a pattern of 'deanimalization' in human evolution. The switch from instinct to learning is the new paradigm introduced by humanity. Associated with this new approach is a drastic reduction in brute animal strength, to the point where the human being is rather fragile relative to other comparable creatures. The removal of the tail fits this pattern closely: it is one of the deanimalized features of humanity.

THE HOMINIDS

About 5 to 7 million years ago the hominid line broke away from the chimpanzees.[5] The first genus of the hominids is called the Australopithecines. The famous Hadar fossil footprints indicate a bipedal locomotion for these hominids about 3.5 million years ago. One striking feature of these fossils is that they contain a small footprint within a larger print, suggesting the playfulness of a child, walking in an adult's footsteps. The Hadar footprints suggest that bipedalism was well developed some 1.5 million years (or more) after the hominids first appeared. Although fossil records for 1.5 million years of hominid history are in effect 'missing,' we are almost forced to conclude that the break with the chimpanzees had led to a bipedal hominid at that time, or very shortly afterwards.

The Australopithecines were small-brained hominids who inhabited Southern and East Africa about 2 to 5 million years ago. *Australopithecus afarensis* had a brain size similar to that of modern apes. As already noted, members of this hominid species walked upright (although there is no obvious reason for the bipedalism, since no tools can be associated with these creatures). How they defended themselves remains a mystery. Why they adopted bipedal locomotion remains a complete mystery. If there was no exploitation of free hands in toolmaking, what advantage did the bipedal locomotion offer? This is just one of many frustrating gaps in the historical record of the hominids. If the Australopithecines did not have a toolmaking capacity, then the innovation of bipedalism is simply anticipating the more advanced hominids, without any great advantage to the immediate species.

The Olduvai Gorge in Africa has yielded fossils that have been designated as the first members of the so-called human genus. (Whether this is in fact an apt or correct classification will be discussed later.) This is the species known as *Homo habilis* and it lived about 2 million years ago. The fossil remains are sparse, and it may be that they actually relate to at least two discreet species. The larger species had a brain size of about 700 millilitres (ml).

It is called *habilis* or handyman because its members made stone implements.

This jump from the Australopithecines to *Homo habilis* is another of the many frustrations in hominid family history. Evolution in this case has generated a 75 percent increase in brain size, but there are no intermediate specimens. One would dearly like to know if there were a whole series of intermediate species in between *Australopithecus* and *Homo habilis*, or whether there were a few profound jumps. Since there is no information we are not in a position to say one way or another. All we can say is that by evolutionary standards the brain increased in size at an amazing speed. Even allowing the maximum 3 million years, the rate of enlargement of the brain is breathtaking.

Homo erectus appeared on the scene about 1.7 million years ago. Its brain is from 800 to 900 ml in size. *Homo erectus* became a worldwide successful species. Next came the archaic forms of *Homo sapiens*, with a brain size of 1200 ml, which is very close to the present value. Then the Neanderthals replaced the archaic forms. They were fully established about 70,000 years ago. The Neanderthals' brains were actually somewhat larger than our own. They used fire and they buried their dead (though there is little information on the significance of burial in their culture). All the precursors to modern humans were skeletally and physically much more robust than we are, and there is evidence that the females were all considerably smaller than the males. The first true humans in the sense of 'us' today – the so-called Cro magnons – replaced the Neanderthals about 40,000 years ago in Europe. But they were also contemporaries of the Neanderthals, and it is not clear just where they came from.

The brain size sequence in the hominids is as follows: *Australopithecus* 400+ ml, which is quite comparable to modern great apes; *Homo habilis* 700+ ml; *Homo erectus* 800–1100 ml; *Homo sapiens archaic* 1200–1300 ml; *Homo sapiens neanderthalensis* 1400+ ml; and modern *Homo sapiens* 1300–1400 ml. Each species appears to have been successful and long-lasting: *homo erectus*, for example, endured for at least 1.5 million years.

The hominids also represent a unique group in that the development of the neocortex is so pronounced that we can compare actual brain sizes, rather than adjusting for size.[6] This points to a third trend in brain development in the mammals. First there is the progression from lower vertebrates to ancient mammals to modern mammals. Then within the modern mammals the primate order accentuates the evolutionary trend of increasing brain size. Then within the primate order the hominid family accelerates the rate of growth, so that from start to finish there is a more than 200 percent increase in brain size. A trend nested within a trend that is itself nested within a trend is powerful evidence for some sort of causality at work.

The entire biological world took 4 billion years to amass 400 ml of brain-power. Then the hominid family took about 5 million years to triple that figure. Even if we just extrapolated the increase in brain size from the earliest lemur to the chimpanzee, we would anticipate the arrival of humanity in over 100 million years' time. As things actually happened, a very profound evolutionary jump has taken place. That this jump should have taken place with the most complex entity known to humankind, the brain, just adds to the mystery. The astonishing rate of brain development in the hominids cries out for an explanation.

In fact hominid history may finally prove quite difficult for today's conventional evolutionary wisdom to explain. "Given enough time almost anything can happen" is part of traditional Darwinian folklore. And over a period of 100 million years the hominid achievement is perhaps plausible on strictly Darwinist assumptions. But over a period of 5 to 7 million years, time is of the essence. Whether we allow for a suite of intermediate species or just accept a few, contingent mutations and natural selection come under severe stress.

If we opt for a lot of intermediate species, then we must accept that the same type of contingent mutation is occurring repeatedly, with no other type of mutations occurring at all, since the anatomy of the hominid family does not change a great deal. Given that there are at least 100,000 genes, and that the same group continuously mutates, we are confronted with a contradiction about what 'contingent' means in the first place. This approach virtually concedes that the mutations were focused. And then it becomes even more difficult to explain why the process of brain enlargement stopped.

On the other hand, if there were only a few intermediate species then traditional Darwinist thought must concede that substantial genetic changes, and the ensuing physical changes, can occur all at once. Again these genetic jumps have to be focused, since at least three major increases in brain size have occurred without any other type of mutation. Worse still, these massive reorganizations have to occur in the most complex of all physical organs – the human brain. If contingent mutations can reorganize large sections of an organism's genes, with the accompanying physical changes, what role does natural selection have in the process? What I am finally alluding to here is the need for accuracy. The larger the genetic jump, the greater is the possibility of error. If large jumps do occur then they must be extremely accurate to begin with, and natural selection is left with nothing much to select.

The fossil evidence is clear in one telling detail. In the hominids, brain size has more than tripled in 5 million years, a fairly good estimate for the average lifespan of just one marine species. This prodigious achievement occurs at the end of the rapid increase in brain size achieved by the primates. And this all takes place in context of the large increase in brain size achieved by the terrestrial vertebrates. It is hard not to conclude that evolution is following some preferred pathway. And this ultimately implies that it is somehow being directed by some form of internal program, or even some purpose or design.

THE ABSENCE OF REPTILIAN INTELLIGENCE

This implication of some programmed logic behind the evolutionary process arises again, if we compare and contrast the development of intelligence in the primates with its lack of development in the reptiles. In the Darwinian world the only source of creativity is the blind contingent mutation: selection only renders a verdict on what has been attempted. The entire primate order is anticipating the evolutionary adaptation of bipedalism. Hominids, however, do not have propriety rights on bipedalism. The dinosaurs achieved it as well.

Recent discoveries of pygmy chimps who are comfortable in a bipedal mode challenge the entire notion of bipedalism as a discriminator between hominids and apes. Bipedalism is highly advantageous in the development and exploitation of intelligence. It frees the hands from heavy locomotory duty and permits them to be used in the business of curiosity and learning.[7] In the absence of heavy locomotory duty the hand is permitted to develop fine movement. The coordination of fine hand movements with the opposable thumb and fine, detailed three-dimensional vision was a landmark development in the evolution of intelligence. It allowed certain creatures to explore their surroundings particularly by being able to touch what they saw. As noted earlier, monkeys exhibit high levels of curiosity by being able to touch what they see, and this trait has persisted in the higher primates.

Human beings are insatiably curious, and without our primate curiosity our intellectual development would have been severely retarded. Being able to see accurately in three-dimensional detail what one can touch and feel in fine detail was a radical departure from the early primates. It was an innovation fundamental to the development of human technology. The immediate application was in making better tools, but later it helped human beings to acquire the ability to write and to learn geometry and other mathematical techniques. Freeing the hands was an aid to exploiting innate intelligence and developing social structure and language. In human language a lot of the talking is done with the hands and the facial muscles. The human face has more facial muscles than any other face in the animal kingdom. Being able to see accurately the fine detail of facial expression and hand movement is a major factor in human communication.

All this would have been impossible without bipedalism, and bipedalism is thus an important and prerequisite condition for the use and development of intelligence. But apparently it is not sufficient in itself, since the bipedal dinosaurs failed to increase their brain sizes. In other respects, however, the dinosaurs were arguably the most successful group of animals of all time. They dominated their world for the entire Mesozoic era, which spans some 160 million years. They achieved remarkable stature in size: Brontosaurus immediately comes to mind. Many of the group were bipedal, such as the infamous Tyrannosaurus with his four-foot-long mouth and undersized fore-limbs, quite incapable of reaching his mouth.

It would seem in this sense that intelligence is not necessarily a prerequisite for dominating one's world: the brain of Tyrannosaurus was as under-sized as his forelimbs. It is also plain that being the top carnivore does not in itself lead to intelligence. The carnivorous dinosaurs were not significantly more intelligent than the herbivores of their day. (And the highly intelligent dolphins, for that matter, have still not displaced the rather brainless sharks in the oceans. Sharks have been top carnivores for hundreds of millions of years, with little if any increase in their intelligence.)

The simple evolutionary fact is that a few hundred million years of reptile dominion on Earth, with some thousands of species, did not produce one line that attempted to evolve greater brainpower. Other things being equal, the smarter animal has the edge. The ancient mammals gave way to the modern mammals. The marsupials of South America gave way to the placentals. One can hardly argue that the economy of the reptile-dominated world operated on fundamentally different principles. If genetic change is due to blind mutation, where are the smart reptiles? In particular, where are the smart bipedal dinosaurs?

This contrasts dramatically with the primates and in particular the hominid family. And it seems reasonable to conclude that reptiles are inca-pable of developing intelligence: the reptile 'experiment' has been run for an immense length of time, with no increase in intelligence taking place. A relat-ed implication is that the higher ranks of the biological classification system (the so-called 'class' and 'phylum,' which I will be discussing in a later chap-ter) set comparatively stringent constraints on evolutionary possibilities. And this again raises the prospect that the process of biological evolution is some-how being directed by some form of internal logic or program, or even some purpose or design.

Proceeding down the same road, part of the logic of being human is a sig-nificant reduction in some animal features. The disappearance of the tail has already been discussed. But there is another most peculiar feature associated with the enormous human brain. One of the functions of the brain is to process information. But all the crucial evolutionary events leading to 'us' today occurred under the subsistence conditions of the Stone Age. And under these conditions it is most peculiar that the creature with the greatest information-processing powers should evolve in such a way as to reduce the sensorial information flow. There can be no argument that human senses of smell and hearing are amongst the least acute of the primate world, even though we have the greatest hardware capacity for processing the information from these senses. It would seem that, under the subsistence conditions of the Stone Age, being able to smell and hear one's prey, as well as to hear and smell one's predator, would have enhanced one's chances of survival. Other animals with trivial brain sizes in comparison to our own have fine-tuned these senses. In human beings, however, they have been reduced.

It is not at all clear how this highly counter-intuitive evolutionary development is to be explained on traditional Darwinist assumptions. In Darwinism, the ability to survive long enough to reproduce and pass on the sacred genes of survival is what life is all about. How can one reconcile the evolutionary development of an immense neurological capacity that has not been pressed into service for the purpose of immediate survival? Even more puzzling is the evidence that, as the neurological capacity grew, sensorial sensitivity declined. Moreover, these evolutionary developments appear to have taken place on a far greater time scale than that required for the immediate survival of any one individual.

When evolution is interpreted as a 'directed' process, the loss of sensorial acuity while the brain is enlarging makes more sense. Here evolution is anticipating the future arrival of humanity through a deliberate process of deanimalization. By removing significant animal powers, evolution forces human beings to make use of their enormous potential intellects. The reduction of animal powers has thrust humanity into self-awareness, self-consciousness, and self-discovery. Just as logical constraints prevented reptiles from developing intelligence, other logical parameters have driven the hominids to develop intelligence. Chance, accident, and contingency play only small parts in this kind of evolutionary process. Each class of organism evolves with an inherent logic built in.

THE BRAIN AND THERMAL CONTROL

Increasing brain size across four classes of animals is one of evolution's great achievements. The brain is out and out the most complex of all organs: the development of such a thing itself borders on the definition of a miracle.[8] And it appears that to develop a larger brain evolution had to induce a quite profound reorganization of life.

As we have already discussed, the reptiles have failed completely to increase brain size in any line at all. Until the emergence of birds and mammals, which only account for about 12,000 species in total, all living things including the reptiles operated at the temperature of their surroundings. Birds and mammals are hot-blooded, and they are the two most recent classes of animals to evolve. The bird's way of life virtually precludes it from evolving a large brain. Flying is a high-energy occupation, and running a large brain is a high-energy occupation. Running the two together would put intolerable strains on the metabolic systems of birds (which suggests a reason why bats, flying mammals, tend to be quite small). Thus birds have maximized their visual powers and have kept a small brain, in a continuation of the reptilian trend. Mammals have gone in the other direction, towards an increasingly larger energy-expensive brain.

Hot-bloodedness is probably a prerequisite for enlarging the brain. The larger the brain the more the demand for a constant body temperature increases. Large brains do not work in wildly fluctuating temperatures. This kind of logic is quite slippery. We only know of large brains in hot-blooded mammals. Not surprisingly, the large brains we know about are conditioned to work under controlled temperatures. There is no law that precludes a large reptile brain from evolving: it just did not happen and hence we have no knowledge of such an entity. All we can really say is that the organization of the large mammalian brain as we know it could not have come about without controlled body temperature. Hence the control of body temperature was a precondition for evolving the large brains we know.

The first hot-blooded mammal emerged as a nocturnal rodent during the time of the ruling reptiles. Between then and the demise of the dinosaurs, no significant evolution occurred. These early mammals made little if any impact and they were not able to upset the rule of the reptiles. Being hot-blooded offered few advantages and they were incapable of developing their latent advantage of intelligence. Hot-bloodedness was a preadaptation anticipating the glory days of the mammals yet to come, but it appears to have offered few advantages to the first mammals. I say this because thermal regulation costs a fortune in energy to maintain, and there must be some payback. But the reptiles held the mammals in absolute suppression for tens of millions of years. Even today, in the age of the mammals, the snake is a proficient killer of hot-blooded rodents. One can only speculate on how the hot-blooded rodents fared in the age of the reptiles, when the snake was but one of many enemies. It is interesting that an instinctive fear of snakes is found in many mammals even today.

It appears there was no significant payback to the mammals who developed hot-bloodedness in the age of the reptiles. They had to hold on to their precarious perch until the reptile dynasty collapsed. The dinosaurs probably collapsed by a gradual cooling of the Earth. The plant life changed dramatically millions of years before the final collapse. The dinosaurs were a pretty tough bunch, and it took the catastrophe of a major meteor impact to drive them to extinction. Only with the world to themselves could the mammals set out on their evolutionary odyssey of increasing brain size.

THE BRAIN: EVOLUTION OF COMPLEXITY

The most complex entity known to humanity is the human brain. The structure and organization of the brain is remarkably uniform. We don't find different brains for different races: all brains are organized on the same pattern. The consistent uniformity of brain form in humankind is conclusive evidence that the brain is coded for by the genes, and not a product of the environment in which humanity lives. Even today we don't know a great deal about the brain, but what we do know makes neuroscience a daunting study. Neurologists have developed their own aphorism on the complexity of the brain: "Anyone who says the brain is complex doesn't know anything about the brain's complexity." Because the cognitive powers of the brain are being used to understand itself, we can never hope to understand the full function of the brain completely. We can understand pieces and segments and some of the complex interactions between different areas, but there is no hope of understanding the functioning whole unless we can somehow get some extra neurons to do the understanding. When we equate the mind to the brain there is an obvious self-reference problem.

The organization of the brain is beyond the wildest imagination of science fiction writers. There are at least 30 billion neurons in the human cortex.[9] A neuron is a specialized nerve cell used in the information business of the organism. It varies greatly in size depending on its actual location and function. Like all cells it has a nucleus and cell body but it differs in having a primary extension out of it, called an axon. The axon varies in length but some are exceedingly long. There are also secondary extensions known as dendrites. The axons and dendrites are used for connecting to other neurons. These connections between neurons (synapses) can vary in type, and can change their type of operation with different stimuli. There appears to be a positive chemical feedback between an axon and the cell to which it connects.

When the synapse or connection fires, the feedback chemical is absorbed by the axon, and this apparently strengthens or maintains the contact or connection if it is used a lot. If the contact is not used a lot the connection appears to wither for lack of chemical feedback. This would appear to be a most ingenious means of streamlining and reducing redundant contacts in the trillions that actually exist. It is possible that each cortical neuron may have at least a thousand synaptic contacts with other neurons. Thus we are looking at something in the order of 100 trillion synapses and upwards in the human brain.[10] This is a minimum estimate because neurons in the cerebral cortex have hundreds of thousands of synapses. Automating the quality of these contacts would appear to be a prerequisite for brain function.

The haunting question is how do 100 trillion plus contacts come into being when there are only 100,000 genes in all?[11] The universal uniformity of brain form among human races is convincing evidence that the brain is coded for by the genes. In evolution how could one increase these contacts by say one percent or just 100 billion? What would guide the additional contacts to their final destinations, and how would the existing 100 trillion contacts already in place accommodate the new material? This is all quite mysterious, and it raises some deep questions about the Darwinist faith that blind mutations alone could assemble this level of complexity, in a time span on the order of 5 million years. There must be some sort of guiding framework for the process, perhaps along the lines of a subtle self-organizing chemical system. Even here we are talking about a level of technology more advanced than anything human beings are remotely capable of producing at present. How could the genes master such a technology by trial and error over a mere few million years?

The brain is organized into major units and then sub-organized into minor units, and this process of sub-organization appears to continue down to relatively small numbers of cells. Each operational unit within the brain has a truly bewildering number of connections to other units and parts within the brain. Many of these connections travel very long distances indeed when the measure of a cell is the yardstick. The pathways for even simple information flow would require far too technical a description for a book of this sort. The only way to summarize the brain simply is to say that it is characterized by an unimaginable number of interconnections between neurons, following a logical pattern of organization compressed into the space of the human skull. Interconnectedness of neurons and miniaturization is the primary characteristic of the brain. Contrary to popular belief, the digital computer has scant resemblance to the brain because it lacks this interconnectedness among the neurons.

How this enigma of the world develops in embryology is quite perplexing. After the central nervous system differentiates, the brain area generates about 250,000 neurons a minute.[12] The ability of each neuron to reproduce or to synthesize DNA disappears and the neuron begins to travel to its final destination. Relative to the size of a cell some neurons travel truly staggering distances. It is believed that they move along supporting cells known as glial cells. Neurons are destined for different sites in the brain according to their date of birth. And it is believed that there is a self-organizing chemical field which directs the neuron on its way. When it arrives at its final destination the neuron begins to associate with like neurons. Again, some form of chemical recognition is involved. Once a group of cells have formed it seems that one cell begins to grow its axon out towards another target-cell group. Once again we have to postulate some form of subtle chemical guide. Other axons from the same unit seem to play follow-the-leader, and they grow their axons somewhat behind the lead axon. A maze of dendritic connections are also made. The next step is to finalize the connections, with much reduction in surplus connections. Excess neurons are removed by what might be characterized as a suicide mechanism. Neurons that have travelled to the wrong destination are eliminated, in a manner analogous to correcting for some overall final blueprint.

How such a contraption can grow in the real world frankly defies explanation. Explaining the evolutionary growth of the brain is even more difficult. In 5 to 7 million years, the largest primate brain grew to triple the volume of the brain of the great apes. This is a momentous evolutionary achievement in its own right, but it actually understates the case. The growth in neural complexity was more exponential than linear. The neurons of the cortex are far more interconnected than other neurons, and it was the cortex that grew in the hominids. As the volume of the hominid brain grew in linear fashion, the growth in complexity approached an exponential curve.

THE BRAIN: AN ADAPTATION FOR INTELLIGENCE

When the individual is born there are no new neurons generated. We start out life with a maximum of neurons and the number is in continuous decline thereafter.[13] But in contrast to quantity of neurons, the quality of the connections between neurons continues to mature throughout the intellectual life of the individual. According to J.P. Changeux:

> The human infant is born with a brain weighing about 300 grams – 20 percent of the weight of the adult brain ... One of the major features in the development of the human brain is that it continues well after birth, for about fifteen years (compared with a gestation period of only nine months). The increase in brain weight does not contradict the fact that the neurons of the cerebral cortex have stopped dividing

several weeks before birth. It reflects the growth of axons and dendrites, the formation of synapses, and the development of myelin sheaths around the axons.[14]

Thus the overall form and structure of the brain is genetically set while the faculty of the operation is influenced by environment. This last point is absolutely crucial: if the brain is not stimulated it will not develop properly. If the eyes are not used after birth then the damage is irreparable. This interplay between environment and heredity is demonstrated by what are known as isolates – humans who have not been reared in the company of others. Perhaps the most famous isolate case is that of Victor, who was cared for by a Dr. Itard, in nineteenth-century France. Victor never managed to fully develop normal intellectual capacities, even though Dr. Itard devoted six intensive years to his care.

Neurons are unique amongst the body's cells in that when they are in place they do not divide and make new neurons. The cells in our bodies are being continuously replaced except for the neurons. Because the neuron has the potential longevity of the entire organism this allows it to develop complex interconnections. Just the thought of trying to get a neuron with 100 thousand contacts to divide makes one shudder. The lack of a neuron life cycle is anticipating the need for continuous growth and streamlining of neural interconnectedness. But the development of interconnections between neurons during the lifespan of the individual is what generates the mechanics of learning – a crucial characteristic of our intelligence. In a sense our brain develops a history of our interactions with the environment through these interconnections. Thus the human brain is adapted to learn.

Indeed, we can make the argument that the brain of a child is adapted to learn language, and the hearing of a child is more sensitive to the higher pitch of the female voice. Hawaiian creole presents a fascinating case study.[15] In order to man the plantations of Hawaii, migrant workers were brought in from different parts of the world. The migrants spoke a number of different languages, and their children, to communicate with one another, seem to have spontaneously developed a creole dialect quite distinct from the original languages of the parents. In fact the parents appear to have had some difficulty in understanding this dialect. But all the children spoke much the same type of creole, with similar syntax , irrespective of the mother tongue of their parents. This is a powerful argument to the effect that the human brain is predisposed to develop language. And language is one of the more significant evolutionary achievements of humanity. Once a structured spoken language develops, alphabets and writing become possible. And as Changeux has explained: "With the development of writing, an extended memory was available to fix images and concepts in a more stable material than neurons and synapses."[16]

Once one says the brain is adapted to learn language one is in effect saying that it is adapted to abstract reality, and this means that it is adapted to be intelligent. Everything about the brain suggests that the brain is adapted to be intelligent. The fact that neural development involves an obligatory cessation of cell replication adapts the neurons for complex interconnections. The development of these interconnections is brought about by environmental influences. Thus the neural development of the brain is an adaptation to respond and learn from the environment.

This aspect contrasts rather powerfully with instincts in animals. Instincts are innate to a species: they are not learned. Insects know exactly what they should do without anyone teaching them. So it is for birds and a host of other animals. But humans have completely rewritten the script, and they rely on learning. The human brain represents the end point in this switch from instinct to learning. The brain is adapted for intelligent functioning. And all of these arguments speak of a purposeful evolution – of a process that has followed some given and particular direction.

When we look at the higher primates it is important to decide whether the animal's intellectual capacity is in equilibrium with its normal way of life. I would answer in the negative. Both the gorilla and the chimp have far too much innate intelligence that is never called upon in their natural setting. A wild horse does not run faster because you tame and train it. In fact it appears that horse breeders have hit a genetic limitation in the speed of racehorses. For years in England, the Derby was run faster and faster, but now the speed has almost levelled out. Apparently the multi-million-dollar bloodstock industry just can't get the horse to run any faster. And this has implications for the natural intelligence of the great apes.

To the best of my knowledge, no researcher has actually tried to breed more intelligent apes, and we can assume that all the research done on apes has been done on 'naturally occurring' creatures. Yet if even half of what has been claimed by researchers about the learning capacity of gorillas and chimpanzees is true, then there is no doubt that they have excess brain capacity on quite a vast scale. The training factor alone could never account for their intelligence. The primates have spent their evolutionary capital enlarging their brains, and hence increasing their ability to learn. They have gradually introduced a new paradigm into biology – the switch from instinct to learning. Progressively, from species to species, the new paradigm was brought into being and reached fruition in the mind and being of humanity.

The learning adaptation has come about by suspending what is characteristic to all other living cells; the ability to replicate. The lack of replication in the later stages of the neuron life cycle is close to being 'unnatural.' The most characteristic trait of living cells is the ability to replicate, and suspension of this fundamental trait alters the fundamental logic of a living cell. The social insects, such as the bees and the termites, have suppressed the reproductive ability of the workers. The workers are slaves to the hive. They work until they are exhausted and then they die. Neurons, in contrast, are prima donnas. They run the show. To build the information processor of our brain this strange adaptation had to come about, in order to generate the number and flexibility of neuron contacts that leads to learning.

This is reminiscent of the pattern of physical evolution discussed in the first chapter. No matter how improbable an event may have been, the laws of physics and cosmic coincidence contrived to bring it about. In a similar fashion biological evolution has historically generated the most improbable adaptations. The suspension of replication in the neuron was so improbable that it appears to be unnatural. But it was absolutely necessary, and it did happen. The right adaptation came about.

THE HOMO GENUS AND THE HUMAN GENUS

Is humanity unique or just the sole survivor of a very unique genus? This question is important in the context of where we belong in the biological order. In particular, what is our relationship to the extinct hominids? Traditional Darwinist thought has classified all but one species of the extinct hominids as belonging to the Homo genus – that is, to the same genus as us. But is this correct? Does it really make, as it were, either scientific or philosophical sense?

Biology employs a highly legalistic approach to classify organisms.[17] Our genus Homo is defined by the characteristics of modern humanity. By the rules of classification, modern humanity is the 'type species' of the genus Homo. And some of the type's key physical traits are: (1) a low measure of 'robusticity,' leading to what has been described as the 'gracile' appearance; (2) a pronounced reduction in the difference in size between the sexes, or sexual 'dimorphism;' (3) near total loss of body hair, particularly in females; (4) no season of heat or 'oestrus' in females, and continuously inflated female mammary glands; (5) several particularly prominent skull features, including a large-capacity convex cranial vault, a 'high-up' maximum width of the skull, a high vertical forehead, an absence of brow ridges, a low rounded 'occiput' at the back of the skull, a projecting jaw, and crowded and reduced teeth in the jaw such that wisdom teeth often fail to erupt properly.

In fact, the architecture of the modern human skull, particularly around the eyes and the cranial vault, is quite different from what we find in the other hominids. In modern humanity, the reduction in the earlier hominids' size of teeth, jaw bones, and other features of robusticity is quite striking. The Neanderthal's tendon connections, for instance, protrude from the bone, indicating far greater strength than we enjoy. The physical power of the Neanderthal was much closer to the great apes than to humans today.

The primates generally are, anatomically, highly conservative as a group: their basic physical plan changes little during evolution. The sum of total change between a monkey and a human is astronomical, but the physical differences are not all that great. Any child can see the overwhelming similarities between a monkey and a human. The physical anatomy of a primate tells us only a fraction of what the creature is or was like. There also appears to be no single conclusive answer to all the provocative questions about the ancestral line that leads to modern humanity. As matters stand, there are four different theories, each with its own merits and flaws. The fossil record of primates in general and hominids in particular is, at best, extremely scanty and highly confusing as well. Any significant new fossil find tends to complicate an already confusing situation. Perhaps the least contentious generalization is that what all the hominids share in common is bipedalism and a large brain.

In any case, since modern humanity is the type species of the Homo genus, one would expect its typical features to figure prominently among other members of the genus. But humanity's quite modest sexual dimorphism is not at all widely shared among hominids at large. The extinct hominids tend to be characterized by pronounced sexual dimorphism: in some cases the males were simply huge in comparison to the females. Similarly, all the apes and all but one of the hominids (modern humans) have or had pronounced brow ridges. Apart from modern humans, no member of the Homo line has had a high forehead and lightly boned convex cranial vault. No other member of the Homo genus has the crowded teeth and projecting jaw of modern humanity. Especially considering that the primates generally are an anatomically conservative order, these differences between the type species of the Homo genus and the other members raise some rather deep questions.

Among the millions of species that have ever lived, humanity is also unique in the degree to which it has come to dominate the planet Earth. One would expect closely related species, particularly at the genus level where interbreeding could possibly take place, to demonstrate at least some of this characteristic dominance. But as best we can tell, there is no compelling relationship at all between the extinct hominids and modern humans in this respect. One might imagine that great care is exercised in designating members of the Homo genus. Yet, as matters stand, the genus's only real distinguishing feature is the size of the brain.

Even here, in biological (and palaeontological) classification generally, when a logarithmic graph of brain size is plotted against the two-thirds power of body weight for closely related species (i.e., those of the same genus), the slope of the line is usually much less than 0.67. As a general rule in both palaeontology and biology, in other words, closely related species have closely related brain sizes. Yet plotting brain size to body weight for the various members of the Homo genus can result in slopes much greater than 0.67. And this implies that, even in connection with brain size, many of the extinct hominids are not strongly related to modern humanity (and in some cases even to each other) at all.

Though it is unusual to use only one distinguishing criterion in biological classification, it is not entirely unique. The flowering plants can be discriminated from other plants solely on the basis of their reproductive system. And feathers are diagnostic to birds. But it ought to be a cause for some considerable concern that *Homo habilis* has less than 75 percent more brain than *Australopithecus*, while the modern human type species of the Homo genus has a 100 percent larger brain than *Homo habilis*. Viewed in this kind of light, *Homo habilis* looks more like an intermediate species than anything else. As Preston Cloud has suggested, it "might as well be called Australopithecus habilis, for it has all the attributes one would expect in a species transitional from Australopithecus to Homo."[18] And Niles Eldredge and Ian Tattersall have argued that

> in fact even *Homo erectus* is substantially more different from *Homo sapiens* (the first-named [type] species of the genus and therefore the one with which all other potential members of the genus are to be compared) than most if not all other mammalian species from the type species of their genera ... we do think that it is wise to bear in mind that the standards of generic classification normally applied in mammalian studies are not necessarily those applied these days in palaeoanthropology. It seems almost as if to exclude various early hominids from Homo smacks of discrimination to the good-hearted liberal sentiments of many palaeoanthropologists.[19]

Some parallel confusions arise in connection with the frequently discussed issue of toolmaking. As I have already noted, the use of tools is not unique to humans or the hominids. Chimps use sticks to get termites, and they can also be induced to learn how to use available objects to solve problems. Seals use rocks to break open shellfish. Birds use thorns as a skewer, and finches in Charles Darwin's inspirational Galapagos Islands trim and use thorns to extract bugs. What makes humans unique is the diversity, sophistication, and complexity of their tools. And tools made and used by the extinct hominids fail to compare with the diversity and sophistication of modern human tools by many orders of magnitude.

A simple 'thought experiment' can help illustrate this point. Imagine that we are making a graph of the complexity of tool technology for each type of hominid and the chimpanzee. We can arbitrarily assign a value of one to human technology. The question is whether any of the other creatures would plot above the base axis? My own answer would be clearly not. Human technology is many thousand times more complex than anything in the past. The primitive stone implements of the handyman just don't measure up. In the space of some 40,000 years modern humans have moved from the 'projectile points' uncovered by present-day archaeologists to the COBE satellite. Even *Homo erectus* remained in a very crude Stone Age for some 1.66 million years. In this setting the extinct Homo species have much more in common with the toolmaking chimpanzees than they do with us. To call the extinct Homo species intelligent apes may offend "the good-hearted liberal sentiments of many palaeoanthropologists" (and of many others among the rest of us as well). But it probably does make a considerable amount of sense.

There is a final and I think quite crucial issue here. One key problem with fossil hominids is typical of any fossil: the so-called 'soft-parts' of anatomy are seldom if ever fossilized. As Raup and Stanley have explained, the "biologist often chooses taxonomic characters based on soft-part anatomy or behavioral traits that rarely leave clues in the fossil record. Problems thus arise in the taxonomy of groups of organisms with both fossil and living representatives."[20] The Homo genus is a particular case in point. Many of the truly distinctive traits of modern humanity lie in soft-part anatomy. (Speech is one very clear example.) So-called 'trace fossils' such as tools can help to overcome this problem. But treating the evolution of human technology over the past 40,000 years as a trace fossil suggests an enormous gap between humanity and all other creatures.

At this stage of the discussion, three questions present themselves. Are humans apes? Are apes humans? And where do the extinct hominids fit in? Quite a lot rests in mere names here, since critical information can be lost by misnaming a creature. As I've already implied, my own view is that on any strict principles of classification the extinct hominids ought to be classified as intelligent apes. And this leaves me with the first two questions to answer.

UNIQUELY HUMAN PHYSICAL FEATURES

Humanity shares an inordinately large brain with the Neanderthals. But there is a great difference physically. The Neanderthals represent the very best case for inclusion in the Homo genus. They had base camps and they used fire, though they probably never developed the technology of starting a fire deliberately. Some less technically advanced human cultures have also had to use firesticks and maintain a base fire continuously. And Neanderthals definitely interred some of their dead: as many as 200 Neanderthal graves have been unearthed. The bodies were normally aligned east–west and their heads rested on a stone pillow. Some implements were buried with them, and perhaps flowers were placed in the grave as well.

On the other hand, if Neanderthal burial was a religious rite – and hence evidence of the capacity for abstract thought so characteristic of modern humanity – why have so comparatively few Neanderthal graves been discovered? The lack of any evidence of 'abstract' art also seems to imply that the Neanderthals were not typically religious in a modern human sense. They do not look like modern humans physically either. They are not at all gracile in appearance. Their skulls are quite different and they have pronounced brow ridges. Their jaws have very large teeth. As noted earlier, the large tendon connections on their bones imply that they were formidably strong creatures. And all this contrasts rather considerably with modern humanity. As Eldredge has argued:

> [Our] different origins, naturally enough, show up in our different anatomies. Especially our brains: Though larger than ours, the Neanderthal brain was differently organized. *Homo sapiens* has a more vertical forehead – mark of a greatly expanded cerebral cortex, the frontal lobes, literally the thinking part of the brain. Neanderthal brains are particularly expanded to the rear – whatever that might imply; but their foreheads slope as did those of their ancestors, and it seems unlikely that they would ever have developed the cleverness that was suddenly to blossom within our own species beginning roughly 30,000 years ago ... I am especially struck by the observation of French archeologist Francois Bordes, who pronounced the rather exquisite "mousterian" tools that were for the longest time the mainstay of the Neanderthal stone tool kit bag as "stupidly"

made. Bordes was not being rude; by "stupid" he simply meant that the neanderthals show no signs of individual creativity and originality.[21]

The one outstanding fossil artifact of the modern humans who came after the Neanderthals is the historical trace of their culture, whether it be seen in the Stone Age cave paintings from 30,000 years ago or the space shuttle today. Perhaps because of my personal professional background, it always strikes me that our exhausted mines must represent the most unique fossil burrows of all time – in terms of their size and depth, and because they have been left in solid rock long after the rocks were deposited. No other creature in biological history has done anything similar. If, at some distant future date, an extraterrestrial anthropologist were to investigate these worked-out mines, he (or perhaps she) would have no doubt about the intelligence of the creatures responsible for them. Our extraterrestrial anthropologist could easily deduce that the creatures who dug these burrows had a vast appetite for the natural resources that energize an advanced technological civilization.

Human beings are intelligent, but they rely heavily on their culture to express that intelligence. Thus those things that promote human culture are critically important. Oddly enough, physical weakness can be an advantage here. Because the human male did not have great strength in his body he was forced to use his brain. He had to solve problems and join other men on the hunt. He had to produce better tools and hunting techniques. He was forced to develop his culture. As with so many cases in biology, there was a crucial 'feedback loop.' Humanity was driven to intellectual self-discovery by the reduction of its brute strength.

Human beings are also the only living naked members of the primate order.[22] Only the elephants and the rhinos share the characteristic of doing without the typical body fur in the terrestrial mammals. It is true that baby gorillas come into the world with only a mop of hair on their head, but they proceed to grow hair quickly. Baby chimpanzees have reduced hair at birth, but they grow hair quickly as well. The nakedness adaptation is readily explained by the overheating problems experienced by the elephant. But humanity does not have a severe overheating problem. And nakedness has been brought to its logical conclusion by human females, who have reduced bodily hair to an extreme degree.

Throwing away the natural fur covering of mammals and becoming naked is probably the least obviously explained adaptation of the Homo genus.[23] The birds and the mammals are the only classes of organisms that use thermal regulation to maintain body temperature above the surrounding temperature. The result of this evolutionary adaptation is that both mammals and birds have evolved an exterior insulation (the fur coat or down quilt, as it were). Even with the aid of insulation, up to 80 percent of a mammal's food intake goes to keeping warm: being hot-blooded is an energy-expensive adaptation. What conceivable sequence of steps in natural selection would lead any mammal to discard its insulation?

As it happens, this question is not addressed to any mammal but to humanity. And Richard Leakey and Roger Lewin have written that: "Matching body structure with ecology and behaviour is inescapable in the context of evolutionary biology."[24] In humanity's case the problem is compounded because of the large brain. Running a large brain is an extremely energy-expensive operation, and it also demands thermal stability. Thus the mammal which could least afford to discard its insulation is the very one that did. This argument must be placed in its original environmental context as well. Human evolution began in the middle of cyclical glaciation. Especially in this harsh environment, removing the mammalian insulation does not make a lot of sense. The layer of fat beneath the skin in humans is a poor replacement for the loss of fur. The far northern Inuit have the thickest layer of fat among humans, but they still require animal skins to keep warm. Polar bears are self-sufficient.

There is almost no apparent evolutionary economy or streamlining for efficiency in the most peculiar adaptation of nakedness. The typical evolutionary pattern, where a creature strives to become perfectly adapted to its environment, seems to break down. What immediate advantage was there for the first humans to be naked? Natural selection has no foresight; it can only operate in the immediate here and now. And this raises another problem for traditional Darwinist thought. In a subsistence Stone Age environment, why should the increased need for food that nakedness induces be some sort of evolutionary advantage?

Yet what we often overlook in the nakedness adaptation is that the loss of body insulation could only work in a creature who is intelligent to begin with. Without the ability to furnish clothes, shelter, or fire in advance, a naked creature would be in crisis every time the temperature went down. Survival requires that this creature be able to abstract the concept of the future. By being born without insulation humanity is forced to provide for the future. The physical limitation of nakedness drives humankind to use its brain to solve recurrent problems of day-to-day life. This in turn focuses attention on the virtues of social order. Base camps and settlements naturally flow from the need to look after tomorrow. Once humanity gets into the business of making provision for the future by developing culture, the great innovation of agriculture looms close enough at hand.

So nakedness forces humankind to create cultural means of providing clothes, fire, and shelter. Just as the loss of brute strength was a deanimalized adaptation, so, too, is the loss of fur. Nearly all other terrestrial mammals use fur for insulation, and the near-total removal of fur in the human reduces this most characteristic mammalian trait. Here, it would seem, is another feedback loop, designed and programmed to promote human self-discovery.

Human females are also unique among all animals, in having no season of heat or oestrus (and, in what is perhaps a related characteristic, continuously inflated breasts). This, to my mind, is one of the most remarkable evolutionary adaptations of our species. It breaks the absolute link between reproduction and sex. While sex is still needed to have children, we no longer need to have children to have sex. The vice-like grip of instinctive behaviour has been broken, and the crucial switch from instinct to learning has begun.

It seems significant that females without oestrus are restricted to the single most intelligent class of creatures. The adaptation of a choice in reproduction is useless unless one can exercise that choice. The exercise of choice demands the ability to intellectually abstract concepts with which to solve the problem: in short, it demands intelligence. Eliminating oestrus is also a precondition for developing a complex social order. Humanity has more than enough difficulty controlling what is left of the sexual drive. Just imagine the chaos a female in heat would cause to a crowded subway train. Humankind could never have built villages or towns or cities with females who had seasons of heat. No urbanization equals no civilization. Females in heat would threaten enduring bonds among male-female pairs. The acculturation of the young would come under great stress. Once such acculturation is minimized, learning is minimized. Humankind could never break out of the Stone Age with females in heat. It is only by removing the female season of heat that the more complex social orders, so typical of humanity as most of us know it today, could ever arise.

In all these respects the loss of a season of heat was a magnificent adaptation. But what use was it in the Stone Age, when modern human evolution began? It requires, for instance, a simultaneous change in the male as well. Other things equal, the female with oestrus is going to produce more offspring to males who are stimulated by the scent. The females not only have to lose the scent, but the males must simultaneously stop reacting to it as well. And this requires some coordinated and balanced evolutionary progression. The reduction in the acuity of the human sense of smell has already been mentioned. It would be impossible to lose the season of heat if the full acuity of our sense of smell had been maintained. What was required was a simultaneous reduction in oestrus and the sense of smell. This, in itself, is quite remarkable. But in Stone Age subsistence living, an acute sense of smell would also have been useful for hunting and defence, and there is no question as to the neural capacity to process the information. Again, the loss of acuity in the sense of smell allied to the loss of oestrus looks a lot like a third deanimalized physical adaptation, acting as a feedback for humanity's intellectual self-discovery. These adaptations are anticipating the advent of civilization.

A final trait that obviously feeds back into human intellectual development is speech. It is impossible to determine exactly when this particular trait evolved, but it seems to be very late in the history of the hominids. According to Eldredge and Tattersall:

> [T]he neuroscientist George Sacher ... has proposed that many of the properties we view today as being uniquely human – language, for example – appeared very late, and only after the brain had reached its present volume ... Interestingly, this notion ties in rather well with anatomical changes to the skull that permit modern articulate speech. These involve flexion of the cranial base to permit the development of a pharynx.[25]

Eldredge by himself has explained how "anatomists have concluded in any case that the human larynx, so crucial to the formation of the vast range of human utterances, was a relatively recent evolutionary innovation, confined in all likelihood to our own species."[26] This implies that the big brain came first, followed later by the power of speech. And this raises the question of why the big brain developed in the first place, and why it stopped growing.

Accompanying the extraordinary increase in brain size among the primates was a parallel trend in physical evolution that promoted the use of the brain. Innate curiosity and colour vision was inherited from the monkeys. They also began the coordination of hand-eye movements and the initial stages of bipedalism. These traits were carried forward by the apes, who probably developed the balance required for bipedalism but not true bipedalism. They continued the use of sound and complex social gatherings. Bipedalism developed in *Australopithecus*, the first hominid. The hands and eyes were probably fully coordinated by the first appearance of the handyman, *Homo habilis*.

Somewhere along this line the use of highly expressive facial muscles to communicate were developed. The vocal chords for exact speech were a very late development, since the great apes are a long way from this adaptation. The development of vocal chords and the brain must have been coordinated as well. As we have already seen the brain is adapted to generate language (as suggested by how easily the Hawaiian children of linguistically diverse parents could create their own creole dialect). But this intellectual talent could go nowhere without the physical means of expressing language. In any case, the three adaptations of reduced physical strength, nakedness, and no season of heat were probably restricted to humankind. The reduction in brute power and the increase in refinement of the human hand were fundamental to the development of toolmaking and all future technology. Physical changes promoted the development of intellectual powers. And the process culminated with the emergence of modern human beings – creatures in the throes of switching from instinct to learning, as they fulfil their destiny of intelligent self-discovery.

INTERPRETING THE TREND TO EVOLVE LARGE BRAINS

The trend in vertebrate evolution to increase the size of brain is undeniable. From fish to amphibians and reptiles to archaic mammals to modern mammals there is a clear increase in brain capacity. Within the primates there is another clear trend of brain-size increase from lemurs to tarsioids to monkeys to chimpanzees to gorillas. Branching off at the chimpanzee is a third trend that is much steeper than the typical primate trend, and this is the trend in the hominids. A trend within a trend within a trend, each more steep than the one before, adds up to a highly focused and concentrated process.

Why did the primates develop their big brain? There is no physical demand so great in the primate environment that calls for this extravagant increase in potential intellectual power. The chimpanzee exists in a simple subsistence mode of life, but his brain is sufficiently complex to solve problems of considerable difficulty given to him by researchers. There is evolutionary overkill in the amount of brainpower each of the primates developed when compared to their mode of subsistence. Evolution appears to go on producing more and more intellectual capacity without any means for the creatures involved to put their intellects to use.

In the economy of the natural world the higher primates, with the exception of humanity, are not particularly important. Their niche tends to be restricted and they are not high on the food chain. Hence, the experiment in generating large brains tends to be a localized affair. Under conditions where brainpower is already in excess, it is more than a little difficult to find reasons why natural selection would be able to select even more brainpower again. The prevailing Darwinian theory demands that there be selective pressure on the increase in brainpower. What could be the selective pressure to increase something that is already in surplus? Both the gorilla and the chimpanzee have intellectual powers greatly in excess of their social structures and their subsistence mode of existence. In the economy of natural selection their very existence is anomalous.

The hominids show a still more pronounced trend towards evolving big brains. The brain is a most expensive organ to run. It comprises less than two percent of man's weight but it costs 20 percent of man's energy to run. Natural selection principles imply that an organ so expensive will operate at maximum efficiency, and streamline away excess capacity. Traditional Darwinist evolution depends on the ability of an organism to pass its genes on to the next generation. Other things equal, the most biologically efficient organism will succeed in passing on its genes.

Yet excess brain capacity is not efficient. The individual with a streamlined brain would have less demand for energy and hence a greater chance of survival in hard times. On these principles the brain would gradually evolve a streamlined aspect with regard to size and energy consumption. Those unable to compete in this sense would be destined for the proverbial graveyard. But this is precisely what does not happen: over-intelligence is the order of the day in the hominids. *Homo habilis* was out and out the most intelligent creature on the planet in his day. What possible selection pressure could have been on him to increase his brain size? This creature had double the brain size of a chimp and close to twice the chimp's intellectual capacity. Yet the chimp himself has more intellectual capacity than he needs for his station in life and is apparently not capable of finding a use for his intelligence. Why would there be a selection pressure for a 100 percent increase in this capacity?

Ultimately the question reduces to whether *Homo habilis* utilized the potential intellectual power that he did have. And the same question can be posed about erectus, the archaic sapiens, and even the Neanderthal. What is most remarkable about all the extinct hominids is how little they did with their immodest increase in intellectual capacity. It seems to me that this feature of hominid history is too often overlooked. The intellectual and technological achievements of our highly encephalized precursors, over a period of more than 2 million years, are extremely slender. Their technology was so primitive that it requires trained experts to distinguish their tools from naturally occurring stones.

In fact, one cannot escape the conclusion that oversized Hominid brains were wandering the Earth for more than 2 million years and they collectively produced a most spectacular intellectual underachievement. That the critical agricultural revolution could not be brought about by any of these creatures over such an immense period cries out for some sort of explanation. The only function of a large brain is its intellectual power. If this intellectual power was being 'selected,' why do we not see the technological fruits that we humans know are associated with the use of knowledge and intellect? The lack of technological development implies that there was no intellectual pressure on these creatures. It is very difficult to determine what exactly was being selected by natural selection.

All the primates are conscious creatures. They are conscious of and react to the stimuli in the real world around them. Humanity shares this trait but the difference is that modern humans have made themselves the object of their own consciousness as well. This means that their consciousness is the object of their own reflection. We are aware of our world and we are simultaneously aware of being aware. Thoughts are the objects of our consciousness, and we can abstract our world. This allows humanity to solve problems that are not immediate. Art and religion are perhaps the most typical early manifestations of an abstract world, but they are apparently missing altogether from the history of the non-human hominids.

Progressive technology is another manifestation of the ability to abstract the real world. And the most important of the early progressive technologies is agriculture. One cannot solve the problem of hunger through agriculture without an abstraction of the problem. There is no immediate solution to hunger by planting a seed in the ground. Indeed the immediate solution is to eat the seed rather than to wait for it to grow. In agriculture the immediate problem of dealing with hunger and the solution are always separated by time. If we remove this element of time we have subsistence living, and this is still the state of all the apes. Without the ability to plan for and anticipate the future, agriculture makes no sense at all, and planning for and anticipating the future is an exercise in abstraction. Agriculture also requires some innate mathematical ability. Simple arithmetic is the foundation of mathematics and it is abstract in nature. Herdsmen need to have some concept of numbers. Farmers need to have some elementary concept of proportion so as to store enough seed to produce the desired yield for a given area.

The evidence is that the extinct hominids had large brain size and small output. These creatures were possessed of great intellectual potential but they failed to develop the most characteristic feature of modern human life, which is some form of knowledge-based culture that allows individuals to learn quickly what their forbearers have discovered. This both preserves what has been learned and provides a base for future improvements. If we tried to build our knowledge from scratch in every new generation, we would never have broken out of the Stone Age. And this is of course the crucial point: our ancestral extinct hominids *were* locked into a perpetual Stone Age. This implies that, despite their huge brains, they were not adapted to learn, because if they had been capable of learning they would have produced some measurable and progressive technology. For better or worse, during more than 2 million years they never did manage the switch from instinct to learning.

The process of biological evolution, one might say, fashioned a magnificent information machine in the heads of our extinct hominid ancestors, but it neglected to provide the key to run the system. And this does appear to contradict the principle of natural selection. From a purely theoretical point of view, at least, what we need is some unequivocal statement from Darwinist thought as to whether evolution must work in the immediate here and now, or whether natural selection has time to render its verdict. Darwinist thought today tends to the view that each adaptation must offer an immediate advantage to the organism concerned. Yet the evidence is that evolution generated a massive surplus of brainpower in our extinct hominid ancestors. In these circumstances I can't see myself what natural selection is supposed to have selected. To me the more plausible inference is that the evolutionary process was somehow anticipating the arrival of humanity.

Modern humans arrived on the scene 40,000 to 50,000 years ago. It is thought that they were probably organized into hunter-gatherer groups comprising not many more than 25 individuals. They had exactly the same brain as ourselves. In less than three percent of the time our so-called extinct cousins of the Homo genus spent wandering around in the Stone Age, modern humans have produced several agricultural revolutions and a quite dazzling variety of complex civilizations, religions, and philosophies. They have the greatest diversity of habitat of any single species on Earth, have now repeatedly succeeded in temporarily leaving the planet, and have developed some formidable scientific knowledge and industrial technology.

In fact, humanity has now embarked on the process of manipulating life itself. In Darwinist terms the genetic mutations that were responsible for human emergence have now come under at least the partial control of humanity. Human beings appear poised to intervene in the very process of evolution, and this places humanity in a unique position with respect to the entire biological world, let alone the apes and the extinct hominids.

Right from the start of modern humanity there was a quickening of intellectual effort. Stone implements improved. The social order became more complex, through the constant use of fire and base camps. Stone Age paintings in caves in France from 10,000 to 30,000 years ago depict not only hunting scenes, but also circular symbols which may have some religious significance (as in some comparable art of the Australian aborigines). These paintings imply an equality between ourselves and these modern humans of the Stone Age – of a sort for which evidence is quite lacking in what we know of the history of the extinct hominids. Compared to their extinct hominid cousins, the Stone Age ancestors of modern humanity took off intellectually like a ballistic missile. On the evolutionary time-scale, going from obscurity to world dominance in less than 50,000 years is comparable to the speed of light in physics. Indeed 40,000 to 50,000 years is so short a time on the evolutionary time-scale that it seems safe to assume humanity is still in the throes of an evolutionary transition. If modern humankind is capable of surviving for as long as its extinct hominid ancestors, then it seems probable enough that it will colonize the bottom of the sea, the planets of the solar system, and perhaps even solar systems beyond.

The brain of modern humanity is more in place today than it was when it first emerged, but random mutations and natural selection apparently cannot look forward. It is more plausible to argue that the brain is a preadaptation for high intelligence. Humanity has passed the last 50,000 years tinkering with this marvellous contraption, and by a process of trial and error has discovered some of its remarkable powers. The powers of the brain were present all along and we are in the process of discovering them. Human history is a process of self-discovery. Again, the intellectual capacity of the brain arrived before there was any means of putting it to use. Stone Age people do not use mathematics, but they may well have had a potential Pythagoras or Gauss in their midst. And the emergence of human intelligence presents us with as fine a case of preadaptation or purpose in evolution as one could hope to find. Though it may strain traditional Darwinist thought close to a breaking point, preadaptation is quite consistent with some form of directed evolution and design.

All this gets us back to the problem of classifying the human animal. Modern humanity has at least three physical properties that could only be supported by an intelligent creature: low robusticity and physical strength, nakedness, and no oestrus or female season of heat. Like the large brain these three physical traits are more in place today than they were in the environment in which they first evolved. They have helped provide the feedback or key to press the brain into service. The human brain was hopelessly oversized for the needs of our more remote ancestors. Modern humanity is only now getting up to speed with its brain. The evolutionary trend within an evolutionary trend within an evolutionary trend paints a picture of a brain growing ahead of any possible use it might have in the environment in which it first appeared. The super-intelligent extinct hominids only managed the most meagre output from their huge brains. Taken all together the evidence implies that the shape, form, and intelligence of humankind was predetermined before it emerged. The evolutionary process was following a plan, and that plan was to generate humanity.

NO LATITUDE IN THE RATE OF BRAIN DEVELOPMENT: THE ECOLOGY ARGUMENT

At the very bottom of the discussion here is the contention that the information-processing machine of an intelligent creature was generated before it was finally awakened. This is supported by the three nested trends in the evolutionary history of the vertebrates, by the surplus of brainpower in the primates, and by the startling rapidity of the enlargement of the hominid brain – generating so much extra capacity in such a short period of time. Much as in the case of the cosmic coincidences discussed in the first chapter, the crucial implication is that none of what has happened could have happened in any other way than the way in which it did happen. And this is the calling card of evolution: the right thing happened at the right time. There is, in effect, no latitude at all. There had to be a final evolutionary sprint in growing the larger brain and in exponentially growing the neural complexity, if an intelligent creature such as humanity were to have any chance of succeeding here on Earth.

There is another ultimate episode in this same story. The conventional Darwinist belief is that evolution will not stop with humanity. When humanity becomes extinct, as all species must, then another intelligent species will evolve in good time to replace humankind. Yet on the argument I am advancing, the great weight of evidence at present implies that if humanity fails and becomes extinct our planet will not be able to support another intelligent technological civilization for hundreds of millions of years, if at all. Indeed an extreme form of this ecology argument would claim that if this present global civilization of ours fails, then, unlike the failures of earlier stages in the evolutionary process, it will find no equal or greater successor. If a knowing observer of creation is the final goal of the process, then humankind appears to be evolution's final creation on this Earth.

Implicit in the Darwinian scenario is the notion of almost practically unlimited time. And as far as the sun goes, this makes sense: it is only halfway through its life cycle. But the affairs of life depend on the heat-engine of the Earth as well as the energy of the sun. Just as the sun has to supply the energy, the Earth has to supply the material in the form of a constant flow of nutrients to the living world. At the moment this presents no problem since the Earth is still tectonically active: we have rings of active volcanoes and mountain building continues uninterrupted. But how long can the heat-engine of the Earth continue to provide life with its all-important minerals? By its nature this is a highly speculative question, and of course no one actually knows the answer. Nuclear fission is the primary source of heat, however, and by the very nature of the 'half life' of radioactive elements (the length of time required for half of any radioactive material to decay), the Earth's supply of heat is in continuous decline. And thus the lifespan of the Earth's heat-engine is quite finite.

There are four rocky planets in the solar system. But Mars has already become tectonically senile: its volcanic activity has ceased and there is no evidence of mountain building going on. Though we know far less about Venus, it appears rather similar to Mars in these respects. Photographs suggest that tectonic activity on Venus has slowed down, and may even have ceased altogether. Gravity surveys indicate that there are no siliceous (or granite-like) continents on Venus, and this implies in turn that volcanic activity there has been far less than on Earth. The lack of a gravity anomaly over elevated areas of Venus suggests that the weight of these areas is fully supported to great depths by the underlying rocks. These rocks must be quite rigid to hold the weight, and this seems to indicate that they do not become significantly hot and plastic with depth.

The point here is that the source of heat is radioactive decay, and hence the heat-engine of the Earth is driven by radioactivity. There is no reason to presume the Earth has any greater concentration of radioactive elements than either Mars or Venus. Thus, while we certainly cannot put precise figures on the problem, we can be sure enough that the Earth's heat-engine has already reached old age. Within 100 to 300 million years it may grind to a halt. Once erosion has levelled the mountains, life on Earth will retreat 'back to the bacteria.' On this interpretation (which is, to be sure, quite speculative), time is of the essence. Planet Earth's ability to sustain advanced life is limited and the clock is much advanced.

Allied to the problem of a possible limited life expectancy of the Earth's heat-engine is the influence of humanity itself. We humans have pressed the bounty of our native planet to the limit. Only with the aid of our advanced technology can we hope to continue prospering and advancing our civilizations. We have mined all the readily available metals. The average grade of ore deposits is steadily declining and the average depth of mines is increasing. In another 500 years, at the present rate of extraction, there will not be a mineable deposit within 5,000 feet of the surface of the Earth.

By the same point in time the fabulous natural wealth of the shield areas will be completely exhausted. Ocean floor deposits will be mined out. All the oil and gas will have been used up within the next 100 years. It has been credibly estimated that we have just 600 years of coal deposits left on hand. And (progressively enough, from one point of view) China, India, and other such places are now rapidly developing highly populous consumption-driven economies, and dramatically accelerating pressure on the Earth's natural resources.

Just supposing, for the sake of argument, that human beings did become extinct in a thousand years' time: how could another intelligent creature evolve and progress in the next 10 million years? Even if such a creature could emerge, what resources would be available for it to use on our own small planet? It seems likely enough that in 10 million years virtually no new metal deposits will be available anywhere on Earth. The Bronze and Iron ages of our earlier human history were facilitated by having copper, tin, and iron readily available at the surface of the Earth. Without metals to make tools, even a highly intelligent new creature would be trapped in some new Stone Age forever.

In the future we humans will have seen to it that all the metals within 5,000 feet of the present surface of the Earth have been removed. A successor species to humanity would have to wait an extremely long time before any new metals appeared on the Earth's surface. Stripping 5,000 feet off the low-lying continental areas of the world and the shields is going to take hundreds of millions of years. And the heat-engine of the Earth may well shut down before then. The technological achievements of the Bronze and Iron ages brought modern humanity out of the Stone Age. But humanity's present much 'higher' technological achievements may well be pre-empting any similar journey by an evolutionary successor.

Of equal importance is the Earth's capacity to replenish its energy reserves. Oil and gas reserves could accumulate over a long time but coal is another matter. It all depends on how likely it is that this aging planet of ours could repeat a carboniferous period when huge quantities of coal were deposited. It could take at least 200 million years for Earth to replenish the bounty of coal we humans have consumed and are consuming still.

This is pessimistic enough, but we have yet to take into account the history of hominid evolution. Once again, the rate of brain development in the hominids is simply staggering. In 5 to 7 million years the hominids have tripled the size of the brain, and the associated growth in neural complexity has been exponential. Assuming that the intelligent successor species to modern humanity is going to start back at some point analogous to the beginning of the extinct hominids, is it reasonable to imagine that this staggering rate of brain development would be replicated? Or would we have to assume a far more gradual development of the new species involved? And under these conditions are we at liberty to assume that the new-species' analogues to the earlier stages of hominid development would do next to nothing with their intelligence, as was the case in hominid history?

If we extrapolate the rate of brain development between the monkeys and the chimpanzee, for instance, it would take at least 100 million years for a new creature as intelligent as humankind to evolve. Under these conditions of gradually evolving intelligence over immense periods of time, it is conceivable that some form of primitive agriculture would be developed by creatures who fall well short of human intelligence. The chimpanzees over the past 5 million years have remained content with a very simple subsistence culture. But if they had the neural capacity of *Homo erectus*, perhaps they could have developed at least some modest form of agricultural technology.

Once our supposed successor species to humankind (with intelligence levels close to those of the early hominids) launched any kind of agricultural technology, some quite major problems would settle in. Our experience today is that we are using up our agricultural soils at an alarming rate. Every time we cut the ground with the plough or overgraze it, we lose soil to the oceans through wind and rain erosion. In a mere few thousand years we have built monuments to our ignorance in the Sahara, the badlands, the denuded mountains, and presently in the rain forests. Mayan and Babylonian civilizations ran into insurmountable problems with their agriculture. In the Mayan world, cities had to be abandoned due to exhaustion of the soil. In Babylon vast areas of production were abandoned due to the build-up of salt, created by the irrigation technology of the famous Babylonian canals. A similar build-up of salt is occurring at present in California.

On a less spectacular scale, all the remaining agricultural soils of the world today are being depleted faster than they can be replenished naturally. And this has happened in a mere few thousand years. Estimates vary, but as matters stand a thousand years seems a plausible upper limit to the lifespan of our current chief agricultural resource. Whether present-day humanity can resolve this problem, while interesting in its own right, is not the issue here. The point is that even a primitive agricultural technology spawned by some less intelligent successor species to humankind would be bound to have some comparable effect over 5 million years. And once all the Earth's soils were depleted, agriculture could never develop properly. In our own experience, at least, without agriculture advanced urban civilization cannot take root. And the only way to avoid this pre-emption of civilization would be for the early intelligent species to do nothing with their intelligence.

Switching our attention from what might happen in the future, we can note that this scenario actually fits hominid history quite precisely.

Intelligence was developed at an enormous speed but, at the same time, it was never pressed into service during the transition from ape to humanity. An exponential growth in neural complexity was generated, without any significant intellectual development actually taking place. Nature (or, if you like, the evolutionary process) held back the key to unlocking the intellectual potential, in the form of the refined human hand, speech, nakedness, and the lack of oestrus or a female season of heat. A similar pattern was noted in the physical evolution of the universe: all the fundamental forces of nature are precisely balanced, so as to maximize complex physical evolution. There was no latitude in physical evolution, and there has been no latitude in neural evolution either. The affairs of the universe, including those of humanity, are unfolding according to an intelligent plan. There is a powerful argument to be made that no second chance is possible. Humanity and its offspring is the final creation of evolution. There is neither time nor bounty left for another intelligent creature to emerge.

This conclusion is dramatically at odds with the received wisdom of conventional Darwinist thought. Had the dinosaurs not been wiped out by a meteorite, then they could have lingered on another 100 million years or more, and humanity or any other intelligent creature would not have had the time to evolve. Had the hominids not had an exponential growth of neural complexity, then the less intelligent creatures would have pre-empted the more intelligent creatures from developing advanced civilizations. The implications for advanced civilizations in space seem obvious enough. If evolution must work to a tight time-line, and at the same time produce a suite of unlikely events, then the number of self-aware and knowing observers in the universe must be correspondingly few indeed. And if this interpretation were to prove correct, then one of the most provocative philosophical thrusts of traditional Darwinian thought – that there is nothing particularly unusual about humanity at all – would also prove impossible to sustain.

Put another way, if the ecology argument holds up, then our present species of modern humanity is an altogether singular entity. We are the only possible knowing observers of an advanced civilization that the Earth will ever be able to accommodate. And this brings us back, once again, to the classification problem of the Homo genus.

It is fairly common knowledge today that the chimpanzee and the modern human have a high degree of similarity in their genetic makeup. At least some more radical Darwinists claim that this means we humans are just rather sophisticated chimpanzees. So Roger Lewin has argued:

> The small degree of genetic distance that separates *Homo*
> *sapiens* from the African apes – just one percent in the genes

that code for proteins – is the same as that often recognized in sibling species, that is species that are barely separate in evolutionary terms ... Pressure is rising to address this issue and to recognize that, in many ways, *Homo sapiens* is really just a rather unusual African ape.[27]

From the point of view of my argument, of course, this genetic closeness must be explained. But one thing it certainly does is confirm my own assessment of the extinct hominids. They must have been even closer genetically to the African apes, and hence it must be not at all unreasonable (or even un-good-heartedly liberal) to call them intelligent apes. And this returns us, once again, to the relationship between the apes and modern humanity.

When the modern human being first appeared, some 40,000 to 50,000 years ago, was it a new type of creature, or are we, in fact, just variants of the modern apes, who nowadays just happen to take trips on airplanes and gaze endlessly at computer monitors? Essentially, this argument boils down to whether the differences between apes and humanity are ones of degree, or whether they involve some new dimension. It seems to me that a species which has the technology to manipulate life itself, and a multitude of other technologies as well, is in possession of an intellectual dimension many vast orders of magnitude greater than subsistence apes. When we look at ourselves in a mirror we can see that a new type of creature has evolved, and it is very recent. And it is merely this very recent splitting off from the ape line that gives rise to the similarity in the genetic makeup of the apes and humanity.

In the end modern humankind is Darwin's missing link, but at the same time we are an entirely new type of organism. What is truly unique among humans is the spiritual dimension, which is perhaps at bottom a result of our self-consciousness. No other animal gives any indication of spiritual activities such as praying. Yet all known human cultures have included a spiritual dimension. Human beings have become so aware of their inner existence – of how they can be both the subject and object of their own reflections – that they seem to have simultaneously become aware of 'Another's existence. Human destiny lies not in further physical evolution but in the spiritual dimension.[28] Humankind is an evolutionary breakthrough. And with this breakthrough the kingdom of the spirit has emerged.

PUTTING IT ALL TOGETHER AND MOVING AHEAD

Our universe must evolve, but only because an unthinkably improbable balance of forces compels it to do so. This is exactly what design and purpose look like. Once again, a purposeful universe is exactly what traditional monotheist philosophy would anticipate. And support for monotheist philosophy is enhanced by the success of such human abstractions as symmetry, beauty, and mathematics in explaining the workings of the universe. These qualities are those of intelligence. It takes an intelligence to comprehend Intelligence. Thus the comprehensibility of the universe argues powerfully for its intelligent design. If the Intelligence of a Creator is discerned in cosmic evolution, then the evolution of human intelligence should be explained by the same hypothesis. What proves compelling is evidence of purpose, preadaptation, and highly improbable evolutionary events.

Fish – amphibians – reptiles – mammals is the known historical evolutionary sequence. Examination of brain development in this sequence reveals a marked evolutionary progression that we can recognize as a trend. Fish have the least brain development, followed closely by amphibians and reptiles. The earliest mammals have a marked increase in brain development over the lower vertebrates. Modern mammals have a marked increase in brain development over the earlier mammals. In the end we have an unambiguous general evolutionary trend towards increased brain development.

Within the later mammals the primate order exhibits another evolutionary sequence of brain development from lemurs to apes. This second evolutionary trend towards increased brain size is far steeper than the average trend in the mammals as a whole. Branching off the ape line, the hominids produced an explosion of neural development and complexity that culminated in the emergence of humanity. More than twice the amount of brain developed in the 5 million years of hominid history than in the preceding 3.5 billion years of biological history, from the bacterium to the gorilla. We are confronted by a trend within a trend within a trend in the evolutionary history of the brain – the most complex entity known to humanity. The key to neural complexity lies in the fact that mature neurons have suspended their ability to replicate like ordinary cells. This allows them to adjust and extend their interconnections with each other, in response to environmental stimuli. The human brain is adapted to learn. And it is particularly adapted to generate language.

Trends in science demand explanations. On the historical evidence the evolutionary process has every appearance of a mission to generate intelligence. Somehow the genetic changes, whether they flow from random or any other mutations, must be purposefully focused to generate the observed historical trends. At first glance this may seem to contradict conventional Darwinist theory, but it is precisely what is required in an internally directed evolutionary process. An alternative avenue is to deny that there is a trend in the first place. Yet in this case the evidence speaks for itself. One cannot go from brain sizes of 400+ to 1300+ ml in 5 million years, with a near exponential growth in complexity, without some concentration of mutations. The purposeful interpretation fits the evidence with considerable ease, while explanations that place too much stress on contingent mutations leave one with one more unexplained coincidence in natural history.

Compounding the problem of the evolutionary trend is the indication that hominid brain development occurred as a preadaptation. Whatever else a process based on contingency can do it can never anticipate the future. The hominids succeeded in developing greater and greater brains but they never realized their intellectual potential. The great apes exhibit an excess of intelligence for their subsistence mode of life. With double to three times as much brainpower, the extinct hominids must have had much potential intelligence that they never actually used or apparently even tried to use. Then why did they develop such a great capacity? How can natural selection select attributes that are already in excess?

Ironically this excess of brainpower is best seen in the success of humanity. The modern human brain is somewhat smaller than the Neanderthal brain. Though it was born in the Stone Age, within less than 50,000 years modern humanity went from obscurity to near total dominion of the Earth. The crucial force driving this success has been modern humanity's talent for using its intellectual capacity. Yet modern humanity's extinct hominid ancestors had an increasingly comparable intellectual capacity for which they never found a use. This implies preadaptation within a purposeful evolutionary process that anticipated the future.

There is some substantial corroborating evidence to support a conclusion of this sort. Bipedalism is an important adaptation in the use and development of intelligence, since it frees the forelimbs for fine work. Why the Australopithecines developed the bipedal gait without evidencing any form of toolmaking remains a mystery, on assumptions that deny some form of purposeful evolution which looks ahead. Why free the forelimbs if they are not going to be used for making tools? Bipedalism was absolutely necessary to future species, including humankind, but it may not have been a significant advantage to the Australopithecines.

Of equal interest is the unqualified failure of the bipedal dinosaurs to develop intelligence. Though there was ample time, no smart reptile ever emerged. This implies some logical or programmatic constraint on the development of reptilian intelligence. And this again suggests some form of purposeful evolution, guided by some programmatic design.

Proceeding down the same road, the present concept of the Homo genus raises some significant problems of classification. In effect, a classification of convenience is sometimes treated as a rigorous scientific classification, which implies that all members of the Homo genus have typical human characteristics. Yet there are some quite striking physical differences between the rather obscure extinct hominids and modern humanity. And, whatever else, modern humanity is formidably capable of using its intellectual powers, in a way that dramatically distances it from the endless Stone Age saga of the extinct hominids.

In the same context modern humanity has evolved a number of physical traits which suggest that it is a quite unique species. Nakedness does not make immediate practical sense for any human being. But it has helped force the modern human species to confront the problem of providing for the future. Similarly, reduced physical prowess and strength would provide no advantage for the typical animal. In the case of an intelligent human being, however, it forces the substitution of brain for brawn. In like fashion, the loss of a season of heat in the modern human female, allied to a parallel reduction in the sense of smell, has helped promote social and cultural complexity. And finally, modern human, social, and cultural complexity has been profoundly deepened and enriched by use of speech and the development of language, which has provided an extended memory for the transmission of crucial information from one generation to the next (and the next and the next again).

In order to generate the intelligent observer that modern humanity has become, evolution had to proceed in the manner it did. Excess intellectual capacity had to develop before the decisive 'final' species was given the key to discovering the intellectual powers in its own head. The ecology argument implies that if self-discovery and intelligence had occurred simultaneously, less intelligent creatures would have pre-empted more intelligent creatures from doing anything with their intelligence. Under the same kind of compulsion the evolutionary process generated an astonishing burst in brain development over the past 5 million years. In order to create an observer-class of creature, evolution had to triple the size and increase by unknown orders of magnitude the complexity of the brain – already the most intricate entity in the known universe. This extraordinary feat had to be accomplished in the shortest possible time frame. This is exactly what did happen and it has every appearance of deliberation. It is quite reasonable to say that modern humanity was intentionally summoned into existence by some form of creative First Intelligence.

All parties to the great debate on this subject are agreed that evolution has succeeded in generating an intelligent creature. For my own part I would add a proposition to the principle of biogenesis: just as it takes a living thing to beget another living thing, so too it ultimately takes an intelligent living thing to beget another intelligent living thing. The cosmos was deliberately brought into being. The comprehensibility of the cosmos comes to an intelligent creature who was deliberately brought into being. The next step in searching for the Creator of this intelligent creature is to explore the more particular process of biological evolution, viewed as the tool of an intelligent Designer.

1   See J.P. Changeux, *Neuronal Man: Biology of Mind* (Oxford: Oxford University Press, 1985), 41–3.

2   H. Jerison, *Evolution of the Brain and Intelligence* (New York: Academic Press, 1973) provides a wealth of information on brain sizes among different classes. Jerison has shown that a plot of brain volume to the two-thirds power of body weight gives a straight plot on a logarithmic scale. Brain volume = $b^{2/3}$ where b is the body weight. When this expression is plotted on a logarithmic graph, it gives a straight line with a slope of 2/3. This relationship allows us to factor natural brain-size increase with body-size increase. When the four classes mentioned in the text here are plotted, there are vertical shifts on the graph, indicating an addition of new neurons for the higher class. Closely related species tend to have slopes of less than 2/3, which would indicate that no new neurons were developed. On the other hand, a slope in excess of 2/3 indicates that additional neurons were developed. It is interesting to note that when we plot representative members of the Homo genus on the graph, the slope of their line is 1.73. And this suggests that the members of the Homo genus were not closely related to each other at all. Much of the subsequent discussion in this chapter is about the mis-classification of the Homo genus, and a particularly useful source for the graph mentioned above is D. Pilbeam and S. Gould, "Size and Scaling in Human Evolution," *Science* 186: 892–901, 1974.

3   P. Naoier, *Monkeys and Apes* (London: Hamlyn, 1970), and F. Szaalay and E. Delson, *Evolutionary History of the Primates* (New York: Academic Press, 1979) are two somewhat older but still useful surveys of primate evolution for general readers.

4   Seeing is believing. The National Geographic Society has developed a video special on "The New Chimpanzees" (produced and written by Catherine McConnell, and directed by Cynthia Moses). Here we can clearly see pygmy chimpanzees from Zaire walking quite comfortably in an upright bipedal posture. They are still "knuckle-walkers" but nearly bipedal when they choose. The video shows much other fascinating and quite remarkable evidence of chimpanzee culture, tool-using, and learning as well.

5   R. Lewin, *Human Evolution: An Illustrated Introduction* (New York: W.H. Freeman and Company, 1984) provides an accessible concise summary of the development of the hominids, with some special attention to the issue of brain size.

6   See Ibid., 81, for a helpful graph of brain size against body weight.

7   See R. Leakey and R. Lewin, *Origins: The Emergence and Evolution of Our Species and Its Possible Future* (New York: E.P. Dutton, 1982), ch. 3, and p. 34, in particular.

8   For a masterful presentation of the brain and its development, see Changeux, *Neuronal*

Man.

9 Ibid., 51.

10 Ibid., 52.

11 See Ibid., 175–180.

12 Ibid., 195–6.

13 Ibid., 197: "We are born with a brain in which the number of neurons can only diminish."

14 Ibid., 198–9.

15 See M. Talbot, *Beyond the Quantum* (New York: Macmillan , 1986), 118–120.

16 Changeux, *Neuronal Man*, 281.

17 Chapters 5 and 6 of D. Raup and S. Stanley, *Principles of Palaeontology* (San Francisco: W.H. Freeman and Company, 1978) give an excellent description of the procedures employed in classifying species and higher orders.

18 P. Cloud, *Oasis in Space: Earth History from the Beginning* (New York: W.W. Norton and Company, 1988), 477.

19 N. Eldredge and I. Tattersall, *The Myths of Human Evolution* (New York: Columbia University Press, 1982), 137.

20 Raup and Stanley, *Principles of Palaeontology*, 125.

21 N. Eldredge, *Dominion* (New York: Henry Holt and Company, 1995), 85.

22 D. Morris, *The Naked Ape: A Zoologist's Study of the Human Animal* (London: Cape, 1968).

23 Traits such as nakedness and the absence of brow ridges are often described as "neotenous," or the retention of juvenile traits in the adult form. Neoteny may be a good description, but it tells us nothing about why these adaptations came about in the first place.

24 Leakey and Lewin, *Origins*, 38.

25 Eldredge and Tattersall, *Myths of Human Evolution*, 158.

26 Eldredge, *Dominion*, 71.

27 Lewin, *Human Evolution*, 21.

28 See P. Lecomte du Nouy, *Human Destiny* (New York: Longmans, Green and Co., 1947). Lecomte du Nouy was the most ardent "evolutionary finalist" of this century. He argues that evolution is going in a particular direction and that future developments for humanity will take place in the spiritual realm.

CHAPTER 3

Evolution:
The Tool of an
Intelligent Designer

As I have made clear from the beginning, my underlying objective in this book is to argue the rational compatibility between monotheistic philosophy and contemporary science, and ultimately to present a case for the existence of a Creator. And philosophically the exercise is constrained by the generally accepted proposition that one cannot deduce the higher order of being from the lower order of being.

In Chapter 1, the big bang and the cosmic coincidences in the evolving universe laid a foundation for my argument. That the cosmos is readily comprehensible to humankind is a powerful indicator of a principle of intelligence at work in the universe.

My goal in Chapter 2 was to link the unambiguous reality of human intelligence, the vehicle through which we understand the universe, to the argument for a Creator. I showed how the development of human intelligence, the child of evolution, has every appearance of having been deliberately brought about.

This points to the proposition that evolution is the tool of some intelligent Designer, since at the very least it did generate human intelligence. The evolutionary process, as it were, is coupled to human intelligence. The next step is to unravel the intelligence factor in the more general process of biological evolution, and in the nature of life itself. To do this one must demonstrate a longer chain of intelligence, running back through evolutionary history to beyond the origin of life. Here in Chapter 3, I am documenting specific cases of biological evolution that create the links in this longer chain.

THE NEAR-PERFECT ADAPTATION OF ORGANISMS

The very notion of the word design conveys the idea of mental forethought or planning. The most daring aspect of the reductionist philosophy in traditional Darwinian thought is the idea that results equivalent to design may be achieved without intelligence. The Darwinist argument for design by blind forces is ingenious. First the random or contingent factor is generated by a genetic mutation. The non-random factor or directive force is natural selection. If the mutation is favourable it will survive and if unfavourable it will die out. Thus if any aspect of an organism such as an organ is under the influence of selection, then mutations in this organ will be highly sensitive. Even the slightest edge on the competition makes all the difference in this case. The organisms with the advantageous mutation will have greater chances of survival than all others. As a result this advantage begins to accumulate in the genetic pool of the species in question. In this way it is argued a blind force can continuously accumulate favourable mutations and in effect produce analogues of design.

All parties, from so-called 'creationists' to Darwinists, agree that organisms, organs, and appendages are superbly suitable for their role in life. Every aspect of an organism is so well-adapted to its purpose in life that it has the appearance of having been designed for that purpose. Darwin mentioned the case of the woodpecker.[1] This bird has a stiff tail that allows it to align itself square to the tree trunk. Two forward and two rearward-facing toes enable the bird to grasp the tree trunk and to remain in an upright position for long periods of time. I have watched a woodpecker stay in a vertical upright position on a tree trunk for well over two hours. The woodpecker is also equipped with a long tough beak that is suitable for boring holes in the trees. Of course going along with the long beak is a long tongue that can be used to pick up grubs at the ends of the holes that are bored.

Even more impressively adapted in my opinion are the poisonous snakes. The majority of snakes are non-poisonous so the use of venom is not an obligatory characteristic of the snake's way of life. Some lizards use venom but its use is most typically associated with poisonous snakes. The poison gland is a modified salivary gland. One of the remarkable features of some snake venom is that it is over-toxic by many orders of magnitude. It is often more suitable for killing an elephant than a rodent. The delivery of the poison is by means of fangs. Some species have back fangs that deliver the poison along a groove. Others have fixed fangs in the front for delivering the venom. The ultimate cadillac of fang adaptation is found in the vipers. These creatures have developed long hypodermic needle type fangs. As the jaw opens the fangs articulate from a sheathed position to an open, ready-to-strike position. This articulation requires a number of moving bones to develop. Once the fangs penetrate the skin the injection of poison ensues. All told, the poison delivery system of the viper is a highly sophisticated and complex mechanical device that is exquisitely engineered for its purpose.

There is no question about organisms being adapted to their environment: this in essence cuts down on my work enormously. I don't need to fill this book with long tedious descriptions of design for a list of individual species. My thesis is that evolution is producing intelligent designs. There is widespread agreement that they look like near-perfect designs. Thus the claim that organisms are near-perfectly designed for their environment is consistent with my main thesis. In one sense this completes the job since we can now say that all of life is displaying evidence of intelligent design. This design was brought about by evolution. This is entirely consistent with evolution being the tool of an intelligent Designer.

We are now in a position to generalize that every species is exquisitely adapted to its role in life. Biologists have classified less than two million species so far, but most scientists would estimate that there are anywhere from two to 30 million individual species living in the world at this moment in time. Each species is superbly adapted to its environment and evolution is responsible for the existence of all of them. Over geological time as many as a billion species have emerged. In the fossil record of geology we do not find mountains of failed prototypes generated in the evolutionary process. The absence of mass failure is a characteristic of the process. In fact evolution has been so successful that one is obliged to recognize evolution as a characteristic of life over geological time. We are even able to calculate average lifespans for species. We can now extend our generalization to include all the species of geological time. During their heyday every one of the billion or more biological species that ever existed was or is nearly perfectly adapted for its role in life.

THE PROBLEMS OF DISCERNING TRUE
INTELLIGENCE IN EVOLUTION

Random events cannot produce the near-perfect adaptation of species. It transpires that there are only two possible interpretations that can offer a theoretical explanation. On the one hand, one can posit the presence of a Designer. The complex ordering and adaptation is the product of the Designer's Intelligence. On the other hand, one can call for self-ordering phenomena of nature. Genetic mutation coupled to natural selection is just such a system. It is a great credit to Darwin and Wallace that they both conceived of a self-ordering system before such ideas had any real scientific currency. Science now fully accepts that self-ordering phenomena can and do occur naturally. The interesting feature of all this is that there does not appear to be any other possible explanation. Other things equal, each side starts out with a 50 percent chance of being correct.

Many writers who object to Darwinist thought have equated the whole process with randomness simply because the mutations in the genes are random or contingent in nature. Darwinist thought does not propose a random system: such a proposition is tantamount to intellectual suicide. Darwinist thinking envisions a self-ordering system based on contingency that can generate analogues of perfect design. Whether one intuitively finds such a proposition to be the same as pulling oneself up by one's bootlaces or whether one finds the proposition to be highly reasonable is almost irrelevant. This is the theoretical position underlying Darwinism, and Darwinists are only called upon to defend this position. Darwinist thought is not called upon to defend randomness in any way at all. The debate has to centre on how to distinguish between two theories that equally explain the phenomenon of near perfect adaptation. Clearly illustrating the presence of near-perfect adaptation in organisms will not work since both theories claim that particular characteristic. Indeed it is because Darwinism claimed it had a theory to explain the near perfect adaptation of organisms that the long-standing argument of design for God's existence has been largely abandoned.

As far as mere design goes, in other words, there is a stalemate in the argument. This is the reason that single examples have proven so ineffective against reductionist thinking on the Darwinian model. Michael Denton has discussed the example of the feather.[2] In this case one has to transform a small dinosaur into a bird-like creature since only birds have evolved feathers. Feathers are made up of keratin, the same protein that makes up the skin of man and the scales of reptiles. Reorganizing the scale of a reptile into the feather of a bird is conceptually difficult. A discontinuity exists between the function of a reptile's scales and a bird's feathers. The scale is used for protection while the feather is for flight. The feather is a magnificent lightweight and aerodynamically efficient adaptation for flight. Some would argue that it is the strongest material for its weight and shape in the biological world. It consists of a strong shaft from which branch out hundreds of barbs. From each barb branch out hundreds of barbules equipped with hooks that mesh with the barbules on the next parallel barb. In flight the feathers are closed on the downstroke of the wing, giving the lift and power for flight. On the upstroke the feathers open, allowing the minimum of resistance to the raising of the wing. To generate this adaptation one must go through a series of intricate changes on the scales of the reptile to transform them into the magnificent aerofoil of the feather. No gradual series of changes would be satisfactory; instead one needs a major reorganization all at the same time. This is immensely difficult to explain but clinching the proof on a single negative is virtually impossible.

Darwin shuddered at the transformations required to evolve an eye. The brain represents the worst case in my opinion. How does one propose to evolve larger brains? There exist a multitude of such cases but they have never been successful in undermining reductionism. One approach would be for a team of biologists and palaeontologists to build an exhaustive catalogue of such cases with the aim of simply overwhelming reductionism by sheer weight of numbers. But even this approach is not guaranteed success. Michael Behe has introduced an alternative approach to the design argument. He argues for irreducible complexity in the field of molecular biology.[3]

Essentially, Behe argues that the proteins of living systems are like machines or complex parts of machines. Many biological structures and systems are made up of hundreds of these proteins. Complex machines or systems cannot be put together by modifying simpler systems. Behe gives an analysis of four such cases: the cilia in cells; the biochemical complexity of blood clotting; vesicular transport or the biochemistry of cell transportation systems; and the biochemistry of select aspects of the immune system. Throughout, Behe stresses that these biochemical systems cannot be accounted for by a gradual mechanism of assembly: they are all or nothing. Moreover, the list is far from exhaustive: the biochemistry of the cell abounds with irreducibly complex systems, and Behe emphasizes that many more examples exist in biology.

All the components of an irreducibly complex system have to be in place before the system can perform the task it is meant to perform. If an extremely complex structure cannot be explained by gradual changes from simpler systems, then it must be the product of intelligent design. Behe has presented the scientific establishment with a major challenge. He is not arguing for one or two difficulties in the mechanics of evolution; rather he is saying that a whole suite of essential but apparently irreducible systems has come into being in the world of biochemistry. Perhaps it is my bias in the matter but it seems to me that science ought to respond to these objections from the world of biochemistry and molecular biology.

Historically it is worth noting that Behe is the third molecular biologist or biochemist to have abandoned strict Darwinism in the more recent past. Crick was the first when he suggested that the origin of life by spontaneous means could be considered a miracle, and then went on to suggest life came from outer space.[4] Denton was the second molecular biologist to abandon Darwinism. Like Crick, he does not appear to be theistic in his approach. Behe is the third and his arguments are compatible with monotheistic philosophy. Molecular biology is one of the more recent sciences and as it has matured it has revealed an awesome complexity in living cells, the very foundation of life itself. Because of this innate complexity in life, I suspect that three defections from the Darwinian paradigm are only the tip of an iceberg.

Gradual evolution cannot explain extraordinary complexity, but Darwinist thought can still argue for self-ordering processes.[5] These type of processes bring order out of disorder or chaos, and thus one is left in the position that reductionism is theoretically capable of explaining perfect adaptation in organisms. However, a self-ordering system and a designed system cannot be identical in every way. A satisfactory way of discriminating between the two theories must exist. The fundamental nature of a self-ordering system gives us the key. Creativity in a self-ordering system is based on contingency. Therefore, if one were to rerun the experiment an overwhelming statistical probability exists that the same result would not recur.[6] In terms of evolution this is the Achilles heel of reductionism. To prevail in the argument I must demonstrate that evolution is producing the same result again and again, or the required genetic change is not contingent.

PROBLEM SOLVING

One of the obvious real-life problems facing organisms is seasonally changing environments.[7] Northern Canada provides an abundance of food of all types during the summer months. It is an ideal place for bringing up young simply because feeding them poses no problems at all. There are numerous studies confirming that the number of eggs laid by birds is proportional to the parents' ability to feed the offspring. Thus a rich food supply during the reproductive season is well worth having. The problem is that there is no food in the winter. The evolutionary solution to the problem is the great migrations of these birds. The Arctic tern covers some 1700 kms in his migration. How he finds his way remains a perennial mystery. But birds, though the archetypical migrators, are not alone in this adaptation.

Insects such as beetles are known to migrate over distances that for us are relatively short but for them must be great indeed. Amongst the fish, herring are well known for their migratory habits. Reptiles are not known to migrate except for reproductive purposes, which is not the type of migration under discussion here. Mammals are famous for their migratory habits as well. The American bison roamed the plains before the coming of the Europeans. The caribou in Canada are still migrating in vast herds over great distances. In Africa the large Savanna animals such as wildebeests and zebras are known to migrate over 1500 kms in response to wet and dry seasons. Some bats are also known to migrate. Migration amongst the marine mammals is common; the Antarctic whale migrates to the tropics. In short, a great number of different organisms have found the same solution to the same problem. Migration is a logical response to an intermittent food supply.

The *alter ego* of migration is of course dormancy. Instead of moving out of a hostile environment the organism adapts by 'shutting down' the system to various degrees. Dormancy that occurs due to drought is called aestivation. It is well known for some frogs and fish to be able to wait out dry months. The more typical dormancy occurs in response to winter conditions. All major groups have species that exhibit dormancy. Snails cover themselves in a thick mucus and wait out the winter. Reptiles and amphibians are renowned for their habit of becoming dormant and they do so automatically. These animals have no heat regulators so they slow down automatically when the prevailing temperature drops. Dormancy is such a powerful process in these creatures that cases are known where lizards and toads hibernate with their arch-enemy, the adders. Presumably they are confident of being first out of bed. There can be no doubt that these are adaptations to hostile conditions.

Some of the hot-blooded animals have adopted the same type of solution. In this case we are dealing with a much more profound adaptation. The very last adaptation of evolution has been thermal regulation in the form of hot-bloodedness. In order for a mammal to hibernate it must turn off the thermal regulator. Normally this means death to the organism, but in hibernation death is cheated. The entire metabolic function and bodily activity slow down to almost a standstill. This is a remarkable adaptation for a warm-blooded creature.

The dormouse in Northern Europe can spend up to six months in a very deep torpor while his southern cousins do not hibernate at all. Why does the hedgehog hibernate while related moles and shrews do not? Why do dormice and hamsters hibernate and related rats and mice do not? Hibernation is not obligatory for warm-blooded animals; it is just one possible solution. Often the exception proves the rule in these cases. Birds are possessed of high-powered metabolisms so as to be able to fly. For years it was believed that birds did not hibernate since it is much easier to fly away than to shut down the thermal regulator. In Alaska and British Columbia one finds an insect-eating bird called the poorwill that was presumed migratory until he was found in a state of hibernation in the field.[8] There is no reason why any bird would go to the trouble of hibernating, but one does.

This strongly suggests problem-solving processes in adaptive evolution. There has to be an internal logic to the evolutionary process that enabled the poorwill to successfully find the hibernation solution to his problems rather than the usual migratory solution used by all the other birds. For a bird hibernation is as unrandom and unobvious a solution as one could hope to find. That so many species of animals come to the same type of solution to an environmental problem lends support to the notion that evolution acts in a logical manner.

Both sides of the debate claim this logic in evolution for their theory. Darwinist contingency can explain many of these evolutionary adaptations but finds it harder to explain why so few birds have resorted to hibernation. There is proof that a bird can hibernate: so why have so few travelled down this path when other hot-blooded creatures have? Arguing it is infinitely more logical for birds just to fly away is tantamount to abandoning the role of contingency in the first place.

One devilish problem for Darwinist thought is that evolution has brought about designs for an environment where no previous store of genetic knowledge existed. We are confident that the amphibians evolved from the fish. The fish has no genetic store of information that would allow it to live on land. The transition to land was completely successful and the earliest amphibians are structurally adapted for life on land.[9] This required evolution to retool the entire fish skeleton that was adapted to the buoyancy of water to cope with the absence of such buoyancy. The flexible swimming spine and fins of a fish had to become the load-bearing limbs and spine of the amphibian. All the amphibian's internal organs had to be supported by the skeleton.

Astonishingly, there are no transition specimens. The entire venture appears to have been brought about both abruptly and successfully. The fossil record is rich in successful evolutionary adventures that have lasted for long periods of time while it is impoverished in short-lived evolutionary failures. Other things being equal, one would have predicted the opposite result from the standard Darwinian theory. Genetic mutations are like blind trials and one would expect a lot of temporarily successful trials to long-lasting successes. This is not the case in the fossil record and it appears there was relatively little trial and error going on in evolution. That there are so few failures and so many successes supports the notion that evolution works logically and not contingently.

EVOLUTIONARY TRENDS IN THE BIRDS

Often we need to give unambiguous examples of evolution at work. Some of the best examples come from work on chicken embryos. It has been found that chick embryos can induce the formation of teeth.[10] No living bird has teeth in any stage of its development. Therefore the power to induce teeth is a throw-back to the past. This is confirmed by the fossil record that shows early birds with teeth. The last bird in the fossil record to have an unambiguous set of teeth is Hesperonis which is found in the Cretaceous period at least 70 million years ago. Clearly the evolutionary trend in all birds has been to replace teeth with a beak. We have found the same sort of thing with bird legs. In the most celebrated ancient bird, Archaeopteryx, the leg is made up of equal lengths of tibia and fibula, the two bones making up our lower leg. It had two ankle bones, one articulating with the tibia and the other with the fibula. The leg of modern birds is now made up of one prominent bone, the tibia, with the fibula reduced to a splint. The ankle, composed of two bones, is fused to the tibia and articulates directly with the foot below. It has been found that a modern chick embryo can be induced to produce the ancestral arrangement in the leg bones.

While we are clearly looking at evidence of evolution in action it is even more clearly a trend. All birds developed a beak made of keratin instead of teeth and they all have the same leg. Yet the ancestral birds had both teeth and two bones in the leg and they produced descendants that converged on the exact same form. This surely speaks of a preferred design at the level of the class *aves* or birds, unless one can make the case that modern birds all come from one line of ancestors. We must remember that in their somewhat short history birds have repeatedly lost the use of flight, but nowhere have they redeveloped teeth or the old leg design. Even extinct birds like Hesperonis show this trend in reducing teeth though they have abandoned flight for swimming. Why some swimming birds did not retain their teeth is quite a mystery in evolution. The normal explanation for teeth loss in birds is that it was an adaptation to increase buoyancy during flight, which is unconvincing in the case of swimming birds. In contrast many of the flying reptiles had to reach enormous sizes before they began reducing their teeth. Birds just seem to have been predisposed to develop a beak.

We can now apply the test for a self-ordering phenomenon based on contingency. Each of the ancient orders of bird that had a jaw with teeth represents an independent experiment in evolution. When the experiment runs its course over time it transpires that the descendants of these birds have all abandoned the toothed jaw in favour of a keratinous beak. Evolution is producing the same result in independent lines, and this is a result that would not be predicted by a self-ordering evolutionary process based on contingency. If there is a general design for a type of creature that we call bird, which possesses a keratinous beak, then this evolutionary history makes more sense.

It is interesting to speculate as to what kind of flyer Archaeopteryx was. This is a vexed question in palaeontology, with opinions ranging from Archaeopteryx was a fair flyer to he couldn't fly at all. Did this ancient bird develop the typical avian lung which is critical for generating high power? The avian lung has a unidirectional flow of air associated with five air sacs in contrast to our own in and out flow. The only evidence we have is the feather and the absence of the keeled breastbone. The breastbone is where the powerful flying muscles are attached in modern birds and it is highly developed. The breastbone evidence would seem to indicate that if Archaeopteryx did fly it did so poorly.

Of course once one comes to this conclusion, which is often disputed, then the existence of the feather is a perfect example of preadaptation for the future high-powered flight of birds. The development of the feather is an anticipation of the future need for a high body temperature, due to high metabolic output and a lightweight aerofoil, and random processes cannot anticipate the future requirements of a new habitat. The feather itself implies some overall evolutionary design as well.

EVOLUTIONARY TRENDS IN THE MAMMAL-LIKE REPTILES

The argument of whether Archaeopteryx was a good flyer or not, and the consequent significance of the feather, leads us naturally into the finest example of underlying design in the fossil record. In deciding whether design produces the adaptations of a creature for his environment or whether the environment selects the adaptations, one needs unambiguous examples of preadaptation. The evolutionary trend of increasing brain size in terrestrial vertebrates, and in particular mammals that eventually produces modern humanity, is a fine example of preadaptation. Another attack on the problem is where one class of animal develops an absolutely indispensable organ for another class of animal and at the same time we can show no apparent advantage to the ancestor. Indeed we may even be able to argue that this was detrimental to the ancestor in question.

With respect to longevity the reptiles were the most successful terrestrial group to ever govern the Earth. Just before the reign of the dinosaurs the mammal-like reptiles gave rise to a group known as the therapsids.[11] They appeared about 225 million years ago at the end of the Permian period. The therapsids exhibit a remarkable evolutionary trend that gradually develops the typical head and in particular the jaw of mammals. One should appreciate that a trend can involve a number of different species, each of which progressively produce an extra component of the trend in question. Each species is stable and successful in its own right. But the trends hops from one discreet species to another.

The changes in the case of the therapsids are especially fascinating. A secondary hard plate in the roof of the skull separated the mouth from the nasal passage. This was an arrangement that allowed the animal to eat and breath at the same time. It is an essential anatomical feature of mammals but not of reptiles. Most reptiles have peg-like teeth while mammals have differentiated teeth consisting of incisor, canines, and cheek teeth. The therapsids developed a similar differentiation of teeth to that of the mammals. The dentary bone of the lower jaw gradually became dominant. In mammals the dentary is the lower jaw bone and much of mammalian evolution is associated with teeth development. In later therapsids the skeleton shows evidence of an advanced upright posture, with both pairs of limbs tucked under the animal.

There is some evidence that the therapsids may have developed some thermal control capabilities. In the snout region there are signs of blood vessels in the form of small pits. The identical pits in mammals serve to accommodate blood vessels, nerves, and whiskers. Whiskers in turn indicate the presence of fur or body hair. Body hair indicates a need for insulation which implies an internal temperature greater than the environment. And this in turn implies an internal source of heat.

In reptiles the articulation of the jaw is between the articular bone in the lower jaw and the quadrate bone in the back of the skull. This is a simple hinge arrangement that allows the animal to either open or close its mouth. In mammals the joint is moved forward and it is more flexible, allowing the animal to chew, grind, and swallow – which contrasts to the reptilian repertoire of bite and swallow. The mammalian hinge is formed between the dentary bone in the lower jaw and the squamosal bone in the skull.

During therapsid evolution the dentary gradually became the dominant lower jaw bone. The dentary bone, which is roughly U-shaped, made light contact with the squamosal bone near the jaw hinge. The reptilian jaw joint between articular and quadrate bones grew smaller and these bones drifted closer to the new hinge point until they were nearly in contact. The ear lies near the jaw joint. Reptile hearing uses a single thin bone known as the stapes. The stapes picks up vibrations from the eardrum and transmits them to the inner ear inside the braincase. The mammals use a vastly more sensitive arrangement of three coordinated bones in the middle ear that are usually known as the hammer, anvil, and stirrup, or the *malleus*, *incus*, and *stapes*. The hammer and the anvil were derived from the reptilian articular and quadrate bones, which had become redundant with the new mammalian joint.

The Karoo beds of South Africa contain a fossil record of therapsids that shows the transition between the typical reptile skull, jaw, and ear and that of the typical mammalian arrangement. It must be remembered that mammals differ from all other land vertebrates in containing three bones in the inner ear. In fact this anatomical feature is so typically mammalian that its presence in an organism today is diagnostic of it being a mammal. In several lineages of the therapsids in South Africa, two bones, the quadrate of the skull and the articular of the lower jaw, become progressively smaller and more intimately associated with the ear region. This of course refers to different and successive species. Finally, when these two bones disappeared as quadrate and articular they became firmly established in the middle ear.

In early stages of mammalian embryonic development the anvil comes from the tissue destined to form the skull, while the hammer comes from tissue destined to form the back region of the lower jaw. These are precisely the areas one would anticipate using the fossil evidence. And the evidence consists of a remarkable sequence of fossil therapsids, displaying a progressive trend in evolving the mammalian inner ear that is confirmed by embryology.

Confronted with this level of evidence one can hardly dispute in any intelligible fashion the validity of major evolutionary change. This is considered by many authorities to be as good as it gets. Evolution is a fact of biological history and it is confirmed by the major evolutionary trend of the therapsids. For those who want to dispute the 'fact' of evolution, this is the case to crack. We are dealing with macro-evolution on the level of the class, which is extremely high. The hearing arrangement of reptile and mammals can be investigated in living members. There exists an unambiguous line of fossils that exhibit sequential evolutionary developments that are confirmed by mammalian embryology. If this is not sufficient proof of macro-evolution then what form must proof take?

The second indisputable point is that this is another example of an evolutionary trend. We have already dealt with the evolutionary trend in brain development that leads to human intelligence, and the trend in birds to replace a toothed jaw with a beak. Now we are confronted with an evolutionary trend in reptiles that leads to a diagnostic anatomical feature of mammals. Something must be responsible for this trend, and the most straightforward implication is that it must be something other than random mutations.

The therapsids present us with evidence of a reptile group that is progressively developing the mammalian ear, or setting the stage for mammalian hearing. Whiskers in the snout area may suggest an increase in the sensitivity of smell. Reptiles' vision is neurologically wired outside of the brain and their senses of smell and hearing are not as acute as mammals. The processing of mammalian hearing and smelling occurs within the brain. This means the wiring is internal to the brain.

Clearly, in order for the mammalian ear to have functioned in the therapsids there would have had to be an increase in the brain size to integrate the sensory information. Yet the therapsids show no evidence of significant increase in brain size.[12] Why would an animal develop the refined sense organs of mammals if it did not have the neurological capacity to process the information? Perhaps the best analogue to this type of situation involves personal computers. The particular software we choose to run is analogous to the sensory information of the ear and nose. The hardware in the form of the Random Access Memory or RAM is analogous to the brain. We are all too well aware that the software programs are getting bigger and better yearly. We can process mountains of information in ways undreamed of only a few years ago. But paralleling the software is the increase in size of RAM. For example, a few years back one megabyte was more than plenty, now the standard is sixteen megabytes. What happens if we load one of these modern programs onto an old machine with low RAM? The wonderful new program crawls through even the most elementary procedures and it takes forever to process a big job. With limited RAM you would be better off with an earlier version of the program which would be able to function efficiently.

In a similar way, without increasing their brain size the therapsids were expending an awful lot of evolutionary capital on unusable innovations. At the same time these innovations have been critical in the lifestyle of mammals. No selective pressure can produce this phenomenon, whereas evolution guided by design can explain the gradual development of the mammalian ear. It is not inconsequential that the mammal-like reptiles collapsed in the face of the dinosaurs even though they had been the ruling class of their day. It is also noteworthy that they became progressively smaller, and this may have constituted a way of providing brain space for the new organs. We are missing the cross between therapsid and mammal, but the first true mammals were tiny shrew-like creatures that probably were active during the night. Another feature that this evolutionary trend demonstrates is that reorganizing brains so that they can expand has some formidable implications. If our class, the mammals, had to begin its existence the size of a shrew, then developing and growing brains is no trivial pursuit.

The therapsid story is a classic in evolution and design. The ear of a mammal is an extraordinarily well-designed and sensitive instrument, but it is of limited use without the mammalian brain to wire it up. The therapsids were anticipating the arrival of the mammals, without any apparent selective advantage to themselves since they became extinct in the process. The selective pressure on the therapsids was leading them to extinction as a group, and this makes the argument that each individual species was being preferentially selected difficult to sustain at best. That the same evolutionary trend leads to mammals supports the notion that the evolutionary process is acting under logical guidelines of design.

SELFISH SEXUAL REPRODUCTION

A crucial characteristic of life is its ability to reproduce itself.[13] There are basically three ways of producing new organisms. The simplest occurs in unicellular organisms like the protozoa, yeasts, and, above all, bacteria, and is called fission. This process can be viewed as part of the growth process. The bacterium continues to grow until it reaches an unstable size and then it divides into two daughter cells. This is an example of asexual reproduction. More complex forms of asexual reproduction common to higher organisms are spore production and budding. Budding as the name suggests is just a part of the parent being used to produce a new individual identical to the parent. Spores are like non-sexual seeds that produce an identical individual to the parent when they land in conditions suitable for germination.

Most nuclear cells or eukaryotes reproduce by a process called mitosis. This is a complex process in which the genes are arranged into chromosomes. Then the chromosomes are copied and a copy of each chromosome migrates to each pole of the cell. With a full compliment of genes at each pole, the cell divides into two identical daughter cells.

Sexual reproduction is the means of producing new individuals in higher organisms. Sexual reproduction mixes the genetic information from two individuals to produce a new individual. In animals specialized cells known as gametes are produced that only have half the chromosomes of the parent. The actual process of producing gametes is called meiosis, and it is a variation of the mitotic process. The cell divides to produce two normal cells. Then a secondary division produces four cells, each with only half the chromosomes. Because each gamete has only half the required chromosomes it must combine with another gamete, containing the complimentary half set of chromosomes.

An interesting aspect of sexual reproduction is the sheer variety of ways and means found in nature. Most organisms above bacteria can reproduce sexually. But plants and fungi can usually reproduce by both sexual and asexual methods. Invertebrate animals in the main reproduce sexually but some can reproduce asexually. Vertebrate animals are nearly exclusively sexual reproducers; but some fish, amphibians, and reptiles can reproduce without mating. The question that Darwinist thought needs to answer is why use sex? The most obvious answer is to provide variation. Sexual reproduction is the source of variation in each succeeding generation. This variation can then be acted upon by natural selection to generate evolution. The validity of this explanation depends upon the validity of gradual evolution itself. Little evidence of gradual evolution can be found in the fossil record. Moreover, this explanation appears to have evolution anticipating the future. Variation can only benefit the group as a whole; it has no obvious advantage to the individual organism itself. Darwinism has difficulty explaining adaptations that benefit the group as a whole, since its conception of evolutionary mechanics works on individual organisms. Yet in sexual reproduction it is the group of organisms that benefits from the variation and not the individual.

From any aspect of natural selection the position of the male in sexual reproduction is highly anomalous. In fact males are virtually incomprehensible in terms of natural selection. In terms of material contribution the male sperm to the female egg is like a pea to a basketball. A sperm is no more than a swimming half-set of chromosomes. The egg is comparatively huge, has its own half set of chromosomes, provides for all the cellular organelles like mitochondria, and looks a lot like a factory ready to begin the process of life.

The contribution of the male to the young in most organisms is almost as insignificant as his initial material contribution. If females became reproductively independent of males then they would not have to share their genes with anyone in the production of offspring. For the exact same amount of work she would double her return, which is not bad by any investment standards. Since Darwinist thought maintains that every organism has an innate drive to leave copies of its own genes in the next generation, then it must be asked why do females keep an expensive male partner? In the Darwinian world of selfish genes, leaving a 100 percent copy of one's genes is preferable to leaving a 50 percent copy.

In this sense Darwinism ought to predict frequent slippage to the condition of asexual reproduction by females. And this slippage ought to occur in spite of any advantage whatsoever conferred by sexual reproduction. Some asexual reproduction actually does take place. There are examples in plants, insects, fish, and reptiles, though the occurrences are not common. (Turkeys, to take one well-known case, can accidentally give birth without fertilization.) The reality is that it takes very little mutating to generate asexual reproduction. Reproductively, the male's role is minimal and could easily be evolved out of existence.

Yet, again, the occurrences are not common: generally this is the very thing evolution has avoided doing. In fact it appears to have conspired to prevent this very thing from happening. For example, in human reproduction, while the male sperm may be tiny in comparison to the female egg, it carries one all-important set of genetic instructions – the placenta. No placenta equals no embryo; the human female has no choice, she must find a male partner. If sex is solely for the purpose of reproduction then this situation is very odd indeed.

Evolution has produced organisms of different organizational complexity. It is possible to arrange these organisms in a sequence from the simplest to the most complicated in terms of physiology. We start with bacteria and end with man. In a general sense, this sequence will reflect the historical evolutionary sequence. It is also possible to arrange organisms in a sequence determined by their behavioural complexity. Behaviour is a trait of organisms that has to be inherited, and therefore evolved. A sequence of organisms arranged according to their behavioural complexity has great similarities to that arranged according to their physiological complexity. This implies that physiologically complex organisms require complex behaviour.

For example, animals are the most complex, physiologically, and they also demonstrate the most complex behaviour. We can also arrange organisms in terms of method of reproduction. We can refine the members displaying sexual reproduction in terms of gender. As we travel up the evolutionary ladder we progress from fission to asexual reproduction, to hermaphroditism, to separate but ambivalent sexes, and finally to obligatory gender. Hermaphroditic reproduction is the rule in lower animals such as sponges and jellyfish. Slugs and earthworms have both sexes but they do not self-fertilize. Hermaphroditism is rare in higher organisms and it is only found in relatively few fish. The ability to 'choose' gender is common in lower animals and gender is often controlled by environmental factors. In the higher animals sex-changing or switching is found in some fish, a family of turtles, and one species of alligator. The two latest-evolved classes of higher animals, the birds and the mammals, are gender-specific.

Over geological time, evolution has gradually introduced gender-specific organisms. If one is to believe that life is a competition to pass on one's genes, and that at the same time sexual reproduction offers the best hope for evolutionary success, then it seems reasonable to suggest that hermaphroditism should be favoured. Hermaphroditism is the best of both worlds: maximum reproduction and maximum genetic variation. The near-useless male is eliminated and the struggle for survival and reproduction is shared by two equal partners. Given the competition to pass on genes, it seems puzzling that this is not the preferred mechanism of reproduction in the general evolutionary process.

If, however, evolution is in the business of generating behaviour, then sexual reproduction is an ideal vehicle. Sex is part of gender but it is not the whole of gender. Nature differentiates between the genders in terms of the roles they play and their characteristic behaviour. The trend in evolution is towards complex organisms being reproduced sexually and we can correlate the most complex behaviour with obligatory gender. Implicit in this notion is the concept that gender roles are a prerequisite for the generation of complex behaviour. Reproduction is the natural order of things in life. When a species is split into two genders, the reproductive drive forces these halves to interact with each other. But the halves are not identical since nature differentiates between the two gender roles. Hence, the reproductive drive compels male and female to interact, even though they may be as different as the peacock and the peahen. Interaction is the prerequisite for behaviour and gender differences enrich this interaction.

Psychologically, humans need to interact with others to acquire a 'psychological mirror' in which to see themselves. The greater the difference in these mirrors, the more one can learn about oneself. It would be stultifying if everyone was the same, and gender differences promise a permanent source of psychological enrichment. One can argue that humanity has brought the behavioural aspect of gender and sex to its logical conclusion. Humans are able to divorce the reproductive aspects of sex from the behavioural aspects. One need not have offspring to have sex. Gender in the higher animals accounts for far more than reproduction: it is the source of much complex interactive behaviour. In my view, sex is a means to generate gender, which in turn serves to induce the complex behaviour of the higher animals. And (of course) this implies that evolution operates according to some plan.

CONVERGENCE OF ADAPTATIONS

The story of so-called 'evolutionary convergence' suggests another kind of evidence that the process of biological evolution operates according to some intelligent design or plan. The key question here is: why do organisms during evolution produce many of the same adaptations?

This is a question frequently evaded in Darwinist thought. Evolutionary convergence occurs when two groups of organisms develop similar features, even though the organisms are not genetically related. Random mutations acted upon by natural selection, acting on very similar organisms in a very similar environment, can conceivably produce the same sort of adaptation. But it is still something of a mystery why the same random mutations should occur in different organisms.

The case of highly dissimilar organisms producing very similar adaptations is particularly difficult to explain. The opposite is equally difficult: namely, why does the evolutionary process fail to produce some obvious adaptations?

So far in this chapter we have been concentrating on evolutionary trends, and I have been making the case that these trends especially speak for logic and design in the process. It is now time to look at specific types of evolutionary convergence that do not necessarily belong to a particular trend.

Myxobacteria and Slime Moulds

The bacteria known as myxobacteria are unique to their kingdom in being able to produce 'fruiting' bodies. Under normal conditions they live as swarms of single cells. When conditions become hostile some chemical signal induces them to form a mound. Then within this mound a stalk-like object is produced, and at the top of the stalk are capsules containing seed cells. The capsules break apart and the seed cells are scattered to more favourable environments. As many as a billion cells can take part in this process.

In the fungal slime moulds known as dictyostellium, individual cells feed on bacteria and grow in numbers by cellular fission.[14] When the food supply runs low a chemical stimulant induces them to coalesce into a multicellular entity like a slug. This new 'creature' moves about until a suitable place for forming a stalk is found. The cells in the head of this slug form the stalk and they do not contribute genetically to the next generation. The cells at the rear of the slug form spores that eventually are released and dispersed to new environments. These two processes are almost unique to each of the kingdoms in which they occur, and at the same time they are remarkably similar to each other. Some unknown logical process is at work when evolution converges across two kingdoms.

Vertebrates and the Adaptation of Flight

Three times in history the front limbs of terrestrial vertebrates were modified for flight. The flying reptiles, the birds, and the bats all achieved similar results. The idea of using wings is common but the feather of the bird is the odd man out. Among the bats and the flying reptiles the front limb developed a sheath or membrane to use for powered flight.

Of all the living things that ever existed, only four groups became airborne: insects, flying reptiles, birds, and bats. Three in this group come from the vertebrates and each member has modified its forelimb for flight. Both the birds and the bats share common features with the flying reptiles, the earliest of the flying vertebrates. Twice, the reptiles developed flight: once with the flying reptiles and the second time to give rise to the birds. What prompted mammals to fly? Whatever the answer may be, one has to admit that evolution is persistent: three times the forelimb of terrestrial vertebrates has been modified for flight, and that makes for impressive convergence in evolution.

Convergences in the Mammals and Two Types of Porcupines

The history of mammals has been dominated by their teeth. One of the most discussed and disputed trends in evolutionary history has been that of the horse. A concomitant trend is seen in the changes that the teeth underwent. As the horses changed their diet to more and more grass, the teeth developed infoldings of enamel to give a much tougher grinding surface. This was necessary since grass tends to have fine silica in its tissue and silica is an abrasive. There is a progressive increase in the complexity of the infolded enamel as the horses became larger. Without its tough teeth, the horse would have no chance of survival: it would literally starve. The bigger the animal, the tougher the teeth need to be. This parallel evolution of tooth to size is as if a genetic program were running its course in the genus.

Many different members of the hoofed animals have developed a similar pattern of size and teeth. Antelopes have developed high-crowned teeth as well. Most of the grazing mammals have independently developed symbiotic relationships with bacteria for the breakdown of cellulose. The horse and the cow use very similar bacteria but in very different locations. In the horse the bacteria reside in the caecum and the colon, and in the cow the bacteria are found in the rumen. We are looking at a very large group of animals both extant and extinct but united by a common plan of campaign. There is an apparent logic to being a particular type of animal that evolution picks up on again and again in different species. But the similarity is never exact: there is always some degree of freedom for the precise specifications of each adaptation.

The porcupines of the Americas, originally South America, and the porcupines of Africa and Asia have remarkable similarities, even though they developed independently of each other and inhabit different niches. The American porcupine lives in trees and the African porcupine lives on the ground. There is great similarity in the internal structural features and general appearances of the two types of porcupines, though there are also differences in the number of digits. The two families of porcupines are so similar that many zoologists used to argue for a land bridge between Africa and North America so the animals could migrate. More recently, however, this interpretation has been abandoned.

When these two animals are attacked they produce the same remarkable defence: they turn their backs to the aggressor. The African porcupine may even try to stab the aggressor with the spine on its tail. Evolution has independently generated the exact same family twice. In the conventional Darwinian evolutionary model, it is quite difficult to comprehend how two groups as far removed as these develop the same unique form and appearance and similar behavioural qualities, and yet occupy different niches. A very similar sequence of genetic mutations must have occurred in both the ancestors of these two families. If mutations are altogether random, the reason for this escapes me.

Two Sonar Adaptations

We take for granted the sense of smell but it has been independently developed and perfected by a great number of organisms. Smell is the chemical perception of the world. Insects and mammals, for example, have developed highly complex smell senses. The termites are blind and thus must rely heavily on smell. Many mammals such as cats and dogs have well over 100 times the human sense of smell. The difference in their perception of the world compares to the difference between a blind man and one who can see. There is clearly a logic to the 'chemical' world that weaves its way through evolution.

Another fascinating use of the senses is hearing. The cats and the dogs previously mentioned also have hypersensitive hearing compared with the hearing of we humans. Perceiving the world via the ears has been brought to an extreme by bats. Bats use sound (high frequency or ultrasound) and the returning echoes of sound, in a manner analogous to the way we use light and vision. A bat must be able to perceive his world quite accurately, since he is capable of catching a moving insect in flight without having a major accident. Catching an insect on the wing is an impressive feat no matter how one does it. The bat is also able to filter out the sounds of other bats. (Otherwise a swarm of them would create mutual chaos, and they would tend to crash.)

The porpoises have developed the use of sound to a remarkable extent. The blind river dolphin or the Susu of India has mastered the art of sonar and has only vestigial sight organs left.[15] Thus the Susu is as deft a master of sound as the bat. Even the sea-dwelling dolphins, however, use the sonar technique with considerable mastery. Richard Dawkins, an eloquent Darwinist, has offered an excellent explanation of the use of ultrasound.[16] But I remain unconvinced myself. For one thing, his argument also demonstrates that evolution has produced the same kind of results in independent trials, and that kind of evidence places a strain on a self-ordering process based on contingency and directed by natural selection. A lot of constraints are at work in the evolutionary process.

Two Types of Camera Eye

Embryology divides the animal kingdom into two distinct sections. In the first are those groups which form their mouth in the first opening that emerges in the developing embryo, and they include most of the animals, except the echinoderms and the chordates. In these last two groups, which constitute the second section, it is the second opening that is turned into the mouth. There are many other important features of embryology that attest to this division of the animal world as fundamental in nature. And this division running down the animal kingdom is a biological Grand Canyon that probably dates back to the kingdom's evolutionary origin. Yet this great biological divide has been crossed by an astonishing evolutionary convergence.

Mollusks, which belong to the first opening section, and vertebrates, which belong to the second, have evolved the same type of eye.

The class of mollusks known as the cephalopods are unquestionably the brainiest invertebrates alive. The most familiar members are the squids, cuttlefish, and octopuses. These animals are on the opposite side of the animal kingdom to the vertebrates, but they have developed an eye structure that is truly comparable to the vertebrate eye. All the basic structures of the eye are present – iris, cornea, lens, retina, and the equivalent of an optic nerve. We have two camera-type eye structures that operate in fundamentally the same manner, though there are some differences in the operation of the retina cells. What type of constraint on the evolutionary process can explain the development of a similarly designed eye in completely disparate organisms? It is at least just as reasonable to argue that some hidden logic is at work as to argue that two independent sequences of random mutations somehow fashioned the same type of visual organ in completely different organisms.

Two Types of Porpoises

Both the reptile class and the mammal class are predominantly terrestrial, but each has evolved members that have abandoned land for the sea. Within their respective marine members, the logic underlying evolution is such that they have conspired to produce a similar streamlined porpoise-type of organism that is capable of live birth. And here I want to compare some features of the ancient Ichthyosaurs and the modern dolphins.

Ichthyosaurs are fossil marine reptiles.[17] They existed for many millions of years during the reign of the dinosaurs. They occupied the niche now occupied by the dolphins. Much like the dolphins, they developed a dorsal fin which was unsupported by any bone structure. That both of these animals developed a dorsal fin unsupported by the underlying skeleton is quite surprising. Both animals came from terrestrial stock, and both added the same anatomical adaptation to their bodies. Moreover, the flipper of the Ichthyosaur had a markedly similar bone pattern and function to that of the dolphin, though the Ichthyosaur's tail had the bone structure typical of a modern shark. Ichthyosaurs were completely marine. No land to marine transitional fossils have been found, and this is a historical feature Ichthyosaurs also share with porpoises. This means that these animals could not lay eggs on land, and since eggs will drown in water, they had to be capable of live birth.

Live birth can take place in a variety of ways between two end-points or extremes. At one end-point, the eggs are held inside the mother in what amounts to an incubation chamber with no exchange of materials. At the opposite end-point live birth occurs with placental mammals, where there is continuous exchange of materials and the young emerge at quite an advanced stage of development. One can find examples of species giving live birth between these two extremes, with some closer to one end than the other.

The earliest Ichthyosaurs had somewhat better limbs than the later ones, and it is possible that they may have laid eggs on land. But their limbs reduced quite quickly, implying that live birth was developed very early on in the history of the group. Since eggs drown in water and they require the ability for gas exchange, the Ichthyosaurs must have converged a long way on the material exchange typical of the placentals. The fossil record tends to support this: it shows two or three young within a mother at the time of death, and in one spectacular case the mother appears to have died during the birth.

The crucial points of convergence between the Ichthyosaur and the porpoise are that: both creatures had terrestrial ancestors yet neither has left any fossils of the transition from land to sea;[18] both are streamlined and appear to have occupied similar habitats; both developed a dorsal fin without supporting bone structures; they have nearly identical bone structures in their flippers; and finally, both developed live birth. Once again the historical record confronts us with evidence that evolution is quite capable of producing highly complex sequences of genetic changes in two independent lines so as to generate remarkably similar organisms. If the genetic changes were altogether random, then one is not in a position to argue that it is either difficult or unlikely for evolution to generate two similar adaptations.

Marine Turtles and the Failure to Evolve Live Birth

Since the Ichthyosaurs evolved the ability to give live birth, it seems reasonable to expect other animals, particularly reptiles, to be capable of some similar evolution if this were advantageous. In fact all sea snakes, the European viper, and some lizards have developed the ability to give live birth. Besides mammals, other organisms that have independently developed live birth are coelacanths, perch, sharks, rays, mail-cheeked fish, brittle stars, and marsupial frogs. I mention these examples of live birth among aquatic animals by way of introducing the particular case of the marine turtles.

The marine turtles have never developed the adaptation of live birth. The oldest marine turtle has an age in the region of 200 million years, which is much the same age as the dinosaurs and the Ichthyosaurs. The group has sat still in evolutionary terms for over 200 million years and has been subjected to the most ferocious predation during its reproduction stage. The birds, and presumably the flying reptiles before them, pick off the eggs and the hatchlings to such a degree that in some cases less than one percent make it to the sea. The mothers are attacked at sea on their way to lay the eggs by sharks and other large fish. Many marine turtles have developed the ability to extract oxygen from sea water along their necks while submerged – which allows them longer periods under water. Yet not one species has developed the obvious adaptation of live birth, which would allow them to stay in the water permanently like the Ichthyosaurs.

Ever since Stephen Jay Gould published his book, *The Panda's Thumb,* in 1980,[19] it has become accepted practice to highlight specific cases of less than perfect design in the evolutionary process as an argument against direct design in nature. The argument is that the panda developed a sixth digit, which is not optimally designed but at the same time an excellent opportunistic adaptation. We ought to be at liberty to use the same type of logic on Darwinist thought and, as in Gould's case, the example should be carefully chosen. I think the marine turtles can take the place of the panda's thumb in a case against mindless Darwinism.

If random mutations under the influence of selection and time can produce all the wonders of biology, why have they not produced live birth in the marine turtles? And let me just quickly work through this, point by point: (1) If random mutations can bring about all the convergences in evolution outlined above, then we are not at liberty to argue that it is somehow unlikely or impossible to evolve live birth in the marine turtles. As mentioned above, other aquatic animals from a wide number of groups have developed live birth and this includes a number of reptiles, including the extinct Ichthyosaurs. (2) More than ample time has been available for evolution to generate the adaptation of live birth in marine turtles – as much as 20 species' lifespans. (3) For the turtles, life on land is only a vestigial connection to their terrestrial past. They have become thoroughly adapted to life in the sea. Land only serves as a place to lay eggs and no more. Thus, there exists a logical impetus to complete their evolutionary journey and break the tie with the land altogether. (4) Natural selection, the key to Darwinist wisdom, favours live birth. Survival rates for the eggs and the hatched turtles are in the low single-digit percentages. Thus every live birth in the turtles would be equal to more than 10 eggs, which amounts to a high rate of return. In the end it seems reasonable enough to suggest that some form of restraint is operating on the evolutionary adaptation of marine turtles. And this restraint has to be internal, within the genes of the turtles.

Two Types of Timber Wolf

Mammals have had remarkable convergences in their history. For example, an ancient group of carnivores had members not unlike carnivores of today.

The equivalent of foxes, dogs, cats, hyaenas, and ferrets were developed. However, the pride of place for convergent evolution has to go to marsupials and placentals. Placentals and marsupials are two distinct subclasses of mammals having live birth. The kangaroo and the wallaby probably epitomize the marsupials. They have the same kind of niche as the antelope and other grazing mammals. They also have a symbiotic relationship with bacteria for breaking down tough plant material like cellulose. Their teeth show the same strengthening which we discussed earlier regarding the horse.

We can make a list of the similarities between marsupials and placentals. The marsupial wombats and the burrowing rodents of the placentals have a lot in common. Marsupial mice are very similar to placental mice though they have different niches. The Tasmanian devil is similar to the wolverine. In extinct forms the marsupials produced animals that appear quite similar to the lion and the bear. The Tasmanian wolf was virtually indistinguishable from the timber wolf of the placentals. Marsupial ringtails and phalangers are strikingly close to the lemurs and the bush babies. The marsupials have produced moles that mirror placental moles in the development of a similar body shape, a powerful digging front limb, and the reduction of vision. The marsupials have produced very similar types of anteaters as the placentals.

The Australian marsupials were completely cut off from the rest of the mammalian world and they evolved quite independently. The truth is that the marsupials have only 250 species in comparison to 3,750 placentals, but they have produced only two unique types of animals: the koala and the honey possum. Every other member of the marsupials shares some to a lot of similarities with the placentals. Two subclasses of mammals have been evolving quite independently and they have produced far more similarities than differences. Being a mammal appears to be a constraint in its own right. Only a very limited number of variations are possible, as the almost identical wolves generated by marsupials and placentals suggest. This same type of constraint pervades all evolutionary convergences, and it is at the very least quite consistent with some concept of directed evolution.

A PARTIAL SUMMING-UP

At this point in the ongoing discussion, I just want to pause for a moment to draw together some of the key threads in the more general argument that is taking shape.

Evolution has generated over a billion species and perhaps as many as three billion, and we are confident that the vast majority of them exhibited near-perfect adaptation. Two possible interpretations present themselves. Either the genetic changes responsible for evolution are operating under internal algorithms of self-organization, which implies that evolution is the tool of some intelligent Designer, or evolution is a self-ordering process based on contingency. Darwinian evolution is a self-ordering system, with the mutation as the contingent and natural selection as the ordering parameter. Both explanations can, in theory at least, produce perfect design, though there are many individual cases, such as the feather, the eye, and the brain, that appear particularly difficult to explain in Darwinian terms. Contingency-based self-ordering systems, however, have a statistical property associated with them, such that if we rerun the experiment in all probability the same result will not occur.

Nature has contrived to rerun the evolutionary experiment a number of times. And we find that, in fact, the same type of result is coming up in different experiments. All the ancestral birds had jaws and teeth while modern birds do not. The descendent lines have all converged on a keratinous beak. Myxobacteria and slime moulds have converged across two separate kingdoms to generate suicidal stalks and fruiting bodies. The same type of eye has appeared on opposite sides of the great divide in the animal kingdom. The great divide, based on whether the mouth occupies the first or second opening, separates echinoderms and chordates on one side with the rest of the animal kingdom on the other. The reptile and the mammal classes have both generated members that returned to the sea. Both produced a very similar marine porpoise capable of live birth.

Similarly, all sorts of convergences appear amongst the mammals. Porcupines, monkeys, and flying squirrels have been produced by different groups. The pride of place goes to the marsupials and the placentals. The less numerous marsupials have only generated two truly distinctive species, while the two groups share an almost identical wolf. The contingency test for a self-ordering system has failed. Indeed, such a breadth of evidence points to precise internal evolutionary algorithms at work. And this conclusion is strengthened by the failure of the marine turtles to develop live birth.

THE SYSTEMATIC ORIGIN OF MULTICELLULAR LIFE

There is a still deeper story to be told here, I think. To no small extent, Darwinism has blinded the world to much of the historical evidence of evolution. Truly extraordinary things happened in the late Precambrian and early Cambrian period of geological history. Over a time-scale of 150 million years, from 550 to 700 million years ago, complex multicellular life invented itself in a frenzy of extravagant creativity. And then the creativity abruptly stopped!

One of the great achievements of geological science has been the compilation of the geological column, which depicts the sequence and thickness of rock types as they were laid down over the Earth's history. Every region has its own specific column, but by means of correlation we can piece together a general column for the Earth at large. The general geological column is full of historical boundaries. By far the most important of all boundaries is that which picks out the beginning of the Palaeozoic era, which is characterized by the appearance of Earth's ancient life. This geological horizon is known as the Cambrian/Precambrian boundary and it takes us back some 575 million years.

Darwinism has a great deal of trouble with so-called evolutionary jumps.[20] Some considerable time ago the geneticist Richard Goldschmidt proposed the notion of 'hopeful monsters' to help explain them.[21] These hopeful monsters are inconceivable within the context of the gradual changes typically assumed by Darwinist thought. As a result Darwinist thinkers tend to resist altogether the notion that large chunks of genetic information can be created or reorganized in a few short steps. The evidence is, however, that rather a lot of successful hopeful monsters have been generated by the evolutionary process.

We know scarcely anything about life before the Cambrian period. There are some snapshots of life in deposits such as the Gunflint and the Ediacaran.[22] We are certain that life was abundant and ubiquitous. The transformation of the Earth's atmosphere occurred in this time. This mammoth task was achieved principally through the photosynthesizing activity of the blue-green algae or cyanobacteria. There was tremendous biological activity during the Precambrian era, but little direct evidence of the organisms involved remains because they had no hard parts suitable for preservation as fossils. The Ediacaran fauna, first described from South Australia, is the group of life-forms that precede the Cambrian fauna. There are now accounts of this fauna from Greenland, Siberia, and England, as well as Australia.

The significance of the Ediacaran fossils is that they represent the first multicellular organisms ever. They are also widespread in their distribution. At the very most the Ediacaran fauna began 100 million years before the Cambrian period. They are entirely soft-bodied creatures. The fossils that make up the evidence consist of trace fossils, that is, tracks, burrows, and impressions of the organisms that had lived in that period. No preserved fossil shells or bones have ever been found.

Where these particular fossils fit into the biological scheme of things is a vexed question. Some authorities consider them to be an entirely novel experiment in life with no modern analogues. Others are inclined to think that they represent members of the coral group with some representatives of the worms and even possibly primitive arthropods. A definitive resolution as to their relationship with the fauna of the post-Cambrian era is presently unavailable. Regardless of which interpretation one takes, it is clear that multicellular life explodes in a creative splurge onto the dying stage of the Precambrian era. What sparked this creativity? The fauna is so widespread that we are forced to look for a global factor. The most conspicuous catalyst for this explosion of evolutionary activity would be geochemical in nature. Most authorities suggest rising levels of oxygen in the atmosphere and the waters. What is incontestable is that the first development of an oxygen-rich environment coincides with the emergence of multicellular life.[23]

The earlier sections of this chapter raised the problem of convergence in evolution. How can one account for the same type of animal being evolved from different classes of animals? The greatest evolutionary convergence ever recorded occurs in the Precambrian/Cambrian transition. This period was the most biologically creative episode in history. It lasted for a maximum of 150 million years. All sorts of organisms generated a multicellular form. During this transition, multicellular life got into the business of inventing itself. We can say this because at the beginning of this phase the logic of a complex multicellular animal phylum did not exist in nature. At the end of this creative stage the logic of many forms of complex animal phyla did exist. The sheer number of organisms that developed this cooperative principle among cells attests to an underlying principle of cooperation in life.

How creative was the event? We have a fossil treasure house in the Burgess Shale of British Columbia that is about 40 million years into the Cambrian period.[24] In the fauna preserved we find all the major animal phyla including the chordates, to which man belongs. The rank of phylum is of singular significance in the economy of life. It represents the fundamental working division of life in each kingdom. The phylum incorporates the basic anatomical blueprint for all subsequent organisms. The evidence shows that all the fundamental anatomical blueprints for animals were up and running by, at most, 40 million years from the base of the Cambrian period, and this figure may be whittled down to 10 million years. Therefore, all the extant phyla that exist today can trace their ancestry to this period. The four major groups of arthropods, for example, are present in the Burgess Shale. Similar fossiliferous deposits have been found in the United States, Greenland, and China, implying that the evolutionary explosion was worldwide.

But the Burgess Shale indicates another more profound feature. There are a number of other phylum-like anatomical blueprints present that never developed into bona fide phyla.[25] Experimental creativity was the order of the day. The striking and irrefutable aspect of this creativity was its success. These hopeful monsters had a worldwide distribution. From the Ediacaran fauna to the Burgess fauna represents one gigantic jump in animal complexity. The conclusion is stark: the evolutionary process is quite capable of producing astonishing jumps in complexity over short intervals of time.

Over the most recent 500 million years, animal phyla have been conservative. Every extant phylum has representatives that trace back over 500 million years in time. All the environmental fluctuations and catastrophes over this immensity of time did not generate the opportunity to produce one single new phylum. Evolution did not stop. On the contrary it transformed the initial life of the Cambrian period into "the ancient life" of the Palaeozoic era.[26] This ancient life then became the middle life of the Mesozoic era, and then this middle life became modern life. The evolutionary process produced new classes, orders, families, genera, and innumerable species – but no new phylum. At present just over 30 animal phyla are recognized. The arthropods represent about 80 percent of all animal species in the world.

We are now confronted with contradictory evidence about evolution. In the last 500 million years the rank of phylum has been conservative and stable, with no new additions. Prior to this, the evolutionary process, starting from scratch, produced many phyla-like blueprints. It also produced all the successful complex animal phyla. The generation of a new phylum automatically means the generation of a new class, a new order, a new family, a new genus, and a new species. A new phylum of any kind entails genetic self-invention on a major scale. Compounding the problem is the fact that evolution is starting from point zero. There are no ancestors from which to inherit the new principles of organization The prospect of generating an entire batch of new phyla blueprints is simply staggering. But it did happen: the evidence is irrefutable. Can there be any other possible explanation of this creativity than genetic jumps and saltations in the ancestors of these creatures? The phyla are the creations of vast genetic jumps, leaps, and saltations, and then the successful phyla are absolutely stable.

Accounting for this situation in conventional reductionist terms is quite difficult. Random mutations are the only source of genetic change in the Darwinian model. The genetic change must occur first, before natural selection can render its verdict. If the change is immediately beneficial to the organism, survival is the reward; if the change is an immediate disadvantage, extinction is the fate. The entire process is blind to the future, and the genetic mutations are blind to everything. During the 150-million-year period that covers the great innovative stage of multicellular animals at the Precambrian/Cambrian transition, the random mutations appear to have gone wild. They are the ultimate source of the creativity that generated many types of animal phyla blueprints. The logic of these new phyla had no prior existence. That so many blueprints were generated testifies to the monumental creativity of evolution. But random processes do not just shut down. Where is the creativity over the next 500 million years? Not one phylum emerged. Any extrapolation of the creativity demands at least some new phyla: and there was ample opportunity, particularly with the great extinctions.

The fossil record is full of extinctions of living things. It is particularly good at recording the history and extinction of animals. For this reason the arguments that follow apply particularly to animals. The record also shows us that there were a number of mass extinctions. We have all heard of the demise of the dinosaurs, but literal Armageddon fell on the Earth at the end of the Permian period 245 million years ago. This is known as the Permo-Triassic extinction and it annihilated 95 percent of all living species. If this event had been a little more severe, then it would surely have driven life on Earth back to the Precambrian era. This is the equivalent of adversity driving modern man back to the Stone Age. Only the hardiest of conservatives survived. Virtually all of the niches on the face of the Earth were left open to new evolutionary experiments. We can be absolutely confident that entire ecological systems remained unoccupied for millions of years while life recovered from this disaster. Opportunity knocked but evolution did not answer: not one new phylum emerged.

Conventional reductionist theory cannot have it both ways. Either phyla are easy to evolve or difficult to evolve, but definitely not both. If random mutations are responsible for the astonishing creative development of multicellular animals during the Precambrian/Cambrian transition, then they cannot just disappear. If rising oxygen levels presented opportunities for creative mutations, then the great extinctions must have provided opportunities as well. Throughout this chapter, I have pointed again and again to the logical operation of the evolutionary process. There is something decisively logical about the same type of creature being developed by different classes of organisms. And this holds for the same type of organ, such as the vertebrate eye, being developed by different classes of organism. Now Darwinist thought must confront the evidence of large-scale evolutionary jumps, followed at a later stage by the absence of large-scale evolutionary jumps. Evolving a new phylum from a zero heredity base is the equivalent of shuffling letters and producing Hamlet. If contingent mutations have the creativity to do this sort of thing repeatedly in one period, how can contingency be shut down in a later period? Just as remarkable is the subsequent stability of the phyla.

The evidence of the past 500 million years is that there are only a select few blueprints of complex animal life that can survive. That there are so few animal phyla speaks eloquently for some powerful restriction on the creative forces of evolution. What is the nature of this restriction? Viability is the most obvious explanation. Viability is a function of the physical environment. Obviously, the environment exerts a restricting force on all organisms. But it works as a negative filter. The environment defines the impossible and therefore acts as a negative controlling parameter on any organism. The physical environment determines what anatomical proposals can survive. Therefore the negative filter of the environment can only control the impossible: it has no input in generating what is possible.

What controls the possible? The only other variable in evolution is the genes. And this implies that the restriction of design as evidenced by the stability of phyla in the fossil record is a genetic restriction. A genetic restriction in the context of random mutations makes no sense. In the world of design, on the other hand, genetic restriction is obligatory. For over 100 years our thinking about evolution has been conditioned by the Darwinian model. We insist on making sense of the evolutionary evidence in reductionist terms, even when there is no sense to be made. The restrictions of the animal-phyla blueprints speak for a Designer in and of themselves. But they also speak of an innate genetic logic to evolution. This implies that biological evolution is a systematic process with very little affinity to contingency. If evolution was causally linked to contingency then new phyla would have been continuously generated, perhaps at a slower rate but certainly not at no rate at all.

THE GREAT MYSTERY OF GEOLOGY

I want now to explore one final mystery of a related type. The base of the Cambrian period is about 575 million years old. For years there were 'unconformities' underlying the Cambrian rocks. In its simplest interpretation an unconformity means that two sequences of rock, one sitting on top of the other, are separated by an undefined amount of time. The implication of an unconformity is that there exists a gap in time between the two sequences of rock. However we now have continuous sequences of rock leading from the Precambrian period through the base of the Cambrian period: the Aldan River sequence in Siberia, for example. In Siberia, close to the base of the Cambrian period, we are able to witness the beginning of fossil skeletons in what is known as the Tommotian fauna. These fossils may be very small mollusks, or more probably they may be entirely different and unrecognizable organisms. Another group that appears is the Archaeocyathids, with no known counterparts. At the base of the Cambrian period the true explosion of skeletonized multicellular organisms occurs.

According to relative abundance, the very earliest bed of fossilized Cambrian sediments contains a number of distantly related trilobites, brachiopods, mollusks, and echinoderm groups. The echinoderms were probably more numerous than their preservation would lead one to believe. They tended to inhabit more agitated waters so that chances of preservation as fossils would be less likely. The very lowest strata have at least 20 distinct species and the general base contains over 60 different species. It is generally agreed that the 20 base members of the Cambrian fauna are so well developed and distinct that they must have had a substantial evolutionary past. But the only trace of a fossilized past is the very small mollusks just under the boundary – if indeed these have any relationship to mollusks at all.

These four advanced animal phyla all converged on the principle of secreting a hard skeleton. In fact most of the logic of advanced invertebrate life-forms demands a skeleton. The skeleton cannot be divorced from the phylum. Just ask yourself, what would a brachiopod look like without its shell? Whatever else it could be, it could not be a brachiopod by definition. Therefore four major phyla all hit on the same idea at what appears to be the exact same time. The mollusks, the brachiopods, and the echinoderms all converged in their ability to secrete carbonate skeletal structures as an integral component of their anatomical design. The mollusks and the brachiopods are the most alike. They incorporated a shell into their fundamental layout, though the shells are different in each case. The echinoderms are radically different. Calcium plates, rather than shells, characterize the skeleton of the echinoderms.

There is no easy way of getting from a shelled animal to an echinoderm. Of infinitely greater significance is the fact that the echinoderms, along with the chordates, are separated from all other invertebrates by the great division of the animal kingdom. This division is so fundamental that it had to occur right at the inception of the kingdom. This means that the echinoderms on one hand, and the brachiopods and mollusks on the other, have virtually no ancestral affinities in the animal world. There is thus no possibility of any inheritance of similar traits from a common ancestor. Yet these disparate organisms simultaneously incorporated a carbonate skeleton as a fundamental and indispensable component of their anatomical organization. If random mutations were the source of this inventiveness then there should, by right, be a graveyard of failed skeletal fossils in the rocks. As it happens, we have no intermediates at all. We can't find any history to the evolution of these phyla. How did three unrelated phyla converge on the idea of fixing carbonate? How did they converge on the idea of using the mineral as an integral skeletal component? That they do so in different ways to each other just adds to the problem. This is intellectual convergence on the idea of a skeleton.

The trilobites are, if anything, even more difficult to explain. They, too, converged on the idea of a skeleton. In this case it is a chitinous skeleton. But this is a throw-away skeleton – trilobites moulted. To make things even worse the moulting in early trilobites was highly complex and was subsequently simplified in later periods. They did not begin with the obvious evolutionary pattern of start simple and end complicated. They reversed the pattern and started with a very complex moult. How complex moulting, with all the attendant enzymes involved, represents the very first attempt at this way of life is a major problem in its own right. The real problem concerns the logic of the skeleton. Again we have intellectual convergence on the idea of a skeleton, but in reality the skeleton of the trilobites could hardly be more different from that of the other three phyla.

These organisms at the base of the Cambrian period are quite advanced in form. It is said that this is indicative of a substantial evolutionary past to each phylum or anatomical blueprint. But this is a case of reductionist theory driving the evidence instead of the other way round. The organisms were not able to inherit the ability to secrete hard-parts from a common ancestor in the immediate past. We have no evidence of any ancestor with hard-parts. The evidence plainly indicates that they have no past as these phyla. The skeleton is an indivisible component to their anatomical layout. If they had a past, then they must have had skeletons of some sort. But we have no skeletons preserved as fossils. Losing all the ancestors of one phylum over a relatively long period of time is nearly unthinkable. Losing all the ancestors of all four phyla over a relatively long period of time is completely unthinkable. The actual evidence does not support in any shape or form the notion of a substantial evolutionary past for the ancestors of these four phyla. Their ancestors must have belonged to different phyla, and once again this implies that the evolutionary process has 'jumped.'

Once again as well, Darwinist thought resists the reality of evolutionary jumps. Conventional reductionist theory just cannot support the notion, since the larger the jump the more irrelevant becomes the ordering parameter of selection. Think of the soft-bodied precursor to the brachiopod. It had to reorganize its entire soft-part anatomy around a shell that had never existed. Each of the four phyla performed the same trick without leaving a mass of failed prototypes cluttering up the fossil record. The emergence of these four phyla represents four major evolutionary jumps. More than a century of reductionist effort has not made the slightest impact on this evidence: it just refuses to be explained away. We have unambiguous scientific confirmation that four major evolutionary jumps occurred.

The next consideration is the timing of the evolutionary event. These four phyla appear in the geological column as if they had just dropped out of the sky. Inexplicably, they all choose to make their debut at exactly the same historical moment. It is their dramatic appearance on the stage of life that defines the beginning of Palaeozoic life. The emergence of any phylum is a major evolutionary event. After the chordates, these four phyla are the most complex and advanced phyla, ever. The abrupt appearance of just one of these phyla is the equivalent of a major earthquake in the biological world. What can one say about the abrupt appearance at the same time of all four phyla?

The simultaneous appearance of these four phyla challenges the notion of contingency in Darwinist thought. The ancestors of each phylum had to begin mutating at pretty much the same time. Even worse, they all had to generate the same spectacular success at the same time, without leaving any failed prototypes in the record. Each phylum represents a vanishingly small statistical probability: the probability that they would all happen randomly at once is smaller still (and probably quite close to zero). Their simultaneous appearance dramatically undercuts the Darwinist argument of choice about time. Random mutations need time to work. Four series of random mutations leading to four new phyla need a lot more time to work. And at the base of the Cambrian period, there is no time.

The final consideration is what unites these four phyla. The principle of incorporating a skeleton is the common new feature of each phylum. This is intellectual convergence on the same idea. There is no possibility of inheriting the principle of the skeleton from distant ancestors. Each of these phyla evolved the principle of an integral skeletal component independently. Each phylum achieved the breakthrough at exactly the same time. Again, random mutations require time to work, but there is no time. They also require ancestors, but there are no ancestors. Mutations are independent events: these genetic changes occur at the same time, which is quite close to a statistical impossibility. The phyla at the base of the Cambrian period are evidence of massive simultaneous genetic leaps in reorganization. And the timing suggests that they are each responding to a stimulus.

The most obvious suggestion is a geochemical increase in oxygen content in the world. Contingent mutations are totally blind. The genes, according to Darwinian reductionism, have no knowledge of the environment, and thus cannot respond to it by mutation. The evidence overwhelmingly suggests that the ancestors to these organisms evolved in response to an environmental change, and they did so at the same time. This eliminates contingency and challenges the foundation of Darwinist thought. Genes developed by contingent mutations can have no knowledge of the future. The ancestors to these organisms were preadapted to evolving a skeleton. The simultaneity of the genetic jumps implies that the genes were predisposed to make these jumps in the first place. When the geochemical conditions knocked, evolution answered. How can there be preadaptation to conditions that never arose previously without intelligent design?

I rest my case on the evidence at the base of the Cambrian period. The test for contingency simply disintegrates under the weight of evidence of four complex phyla – all converging on the intellectual concept of a skeleton at the same time, in response to the same geochemical stimulus. The ancestors of these four complex phyla were predisposed to evolve skeletons when the right environmental conditions prevailed: but these conditions had never before existed on Earth. This is a case of intelligent preadaptation which requires knowledge of the future. Biological evolution has been led by evolution's hand.

A FINAL FOOTNOTE ON BEHE'S CORROBORATION FOR INTELLIGENT DESIGN

As I noted in my early discussion of evolutionary design, Michael Behe has recently introduced the concept of irreducible complexity.[27] He defines this as a system composed of a number of well-matched, interacting parts that each contributes to the basic function of the system, such that the removal of one component causes the system to stop functioning.

Instead of focusing on macroscopic systems, as I have been doing in this chapter, Behe takes up microscopic systems in molecular biology. He argues that blood coagulation and the immune system in multicellular animals, which came late in the history of life, could not be produced by any gradual model: they must have come into being all at once.

For my own arguments, Behe's work implies either that evolution is an intelligently designed process, producing such intelligent results as irreducibly complex systems, or that no evolution has taken place in biological history at all. And of course to say that there has been no evolution plainly contradicts the fossil record. The genes of modern creatures themselves are not 'clean': they bear the scars of evolutionary history in the form of junk material and 'pseudo-genes.' (And even for monotheist philosophers who might care nothing for contemporary science, to say that there has been no evolution would present a picture of a highly uncertain Creator fumbling through biological history: when one line of trilobites dies out, the Creator would have to wake up and create another.)

Once again this leaves us with the implication that evolution is the tool of some intelligent Designer. My arguments in this chapter have been based on macroscopic features such as skeleton, limbs, and organs, while Behe has concentrated on the molecular level of proteins. Yet if Behe's arguments stand up to sustained scrutiny, and I strongly believe they will, his microscopic concept can only serve to reinforce my macroscopic claims.

THE INTELLIGENT DESIGNER MOVES ON

To sum-up the ongoing thrust of the argument in the first half of this book, the universe began in what looks like an act of creation: there was a time when there was no before. Our physical universe is compelled to evolve by the existence of razor-edged balances in the fundamental forces of nature. The ultimate incomprehensibility confronting science is simply that the universe is comprehensible. Our ability to understand so much of the workings of the cosmos is the strongest argument for the existence of an Intelligence behind the workings of the universe. If one posits a Creator, then physical evolution is one of this Creator's tools. But the comprehending mind on this Earth is the product of biological evolution. This leads us to the proposition that biological evolution is also the tool of an intelligent Designer.

When we examine the emergence of intelligence on Earth the case for a principle similar to biogenesis is strong. Just as it takes living things to beget other living things, it also takes Intelligence to beget intelligence. And there is an unambiguous trend towards increasing intelligence in biological history. The last five million years of this trend is marked by an exponential growth in neural complexity. And finally, the modern human brain becomes adapted to learn. The neuron can no longer synthesize DNA like other cells. Instead, it has the potential longevity of the human being, and the quality of its interconnections to other neurons changes in response to environmental influences – a learning adaptation.

The great brain of the hominids was a preadaptation because they never did anything with their intellectual capacity. This is dramatized by the explosive success of modern humanity. In 50,000 years humanity went from obscurity to supremacy and its success is directly attributable to its intellectual powers. Unlike its extinct hominid ancestors, modern humanity was designed to harness its intellectual powers. Reduced animal strength, nakedness, and lack of a female season of heat all helped to force humankind to substitute brain for brawn. The evolutionary process furnished us with physical traits that compelled us to discover our intellectual powers. The human being was forced into self-discovery and it all looks utterly purposeful. The hand of a Creator can be discerned. The cosmos was deliberately brought into being. The comprehensibility of the cosmos becomes clear to a creature who was deliberately brought into being to comprehend it.

The next step in the search for the Creator was to explore biological evolution as the tool of an intelligent Designer. The evolutionary process has generated over a billion near-perfectly adapted species. Either the genetic changes responsible for evolution are operating under internal algorithms of self-organization, which means evolution is the tool of an intelligent

Designer, or evolution is a self-ordering process based on contingency. Both explanations can theoretically produce near-perfect designs (though many individual evolutionary cases present some particular problems for conventional Darwinist thought). But contingent self-ordering systems have a statistical property associated with them, such that if we rerun the experiment, in all probability the same result will not occur.

In a number of cases evolution actually has rerun the experiment a number of times and the same type of result has appeared. All the ancestral birds had jaws and teeth while modern birds do not. The descendent lines have all converged on a keratinous beak. Myxobacteria and slime moulds have converged across two separate kingdoms to generate suicidal stalks and fruiting bodies. The exact same eye has appeared on opposite sides of the great division in the animal kingdom. The reptiles and the mammal class have both generated members that returned to the sea. Both the reptile and the mammal class generated a streamlined marine porpoise-type of creature, capable of live birth, with an unsupported dorsal fin. At the same time, marine turtles never developed the adaptation of live birth. There are all sorts of convergences amongst the mammals. Porcupines, monkeys, and flying squirrels have been produced by different groups. The pride of place goes to the marsupials and the placentals. The less numerous marsupials have only generated two truly distinctive species, while the two groups share an almost identical wolf.

The emergence of multicellular life confirms evolution as a systematic process. From a zero heredity base many different animal phyla evolved in 150 million years near the Precambrian/Cambrian transition. Yet over the last 500 million years evolutionary creativity at the level of phylum has stalled. The specific case of the four phyla of arthropods, mollusks, brachiopods, and echinoderms – exploding onto the scene at the base of the Cambrian period – is highly provocative. All four evolved simultaneously and they all display convergence in organization: they have all reorganized their anatomy around a skeleton. Although advanced in form, not one of the four has any skeletonized ancestors. It seems that these organisms evolved in response to the environmental stimulus of increasing levels of oxygen.

On conventional Darwinist assumptions, genes cannot respond to the environment: genetic change must be a contingent mutation. It is statistically improbable in the extreme to have four strikes of lightning at the very same time, and it would amount to an extraordinary coincidence if contingent mutations were to explain what happened at the base of the Cambrian period. Each of the organisms had to be retooled on an enormous scale so as to incorporate a skeleton in its design. This speaks of massive genetic change in the ancestral species. One such genetic leap would be highly anomalous. Four such leaps speak of a predisposition in the genes to evolve. Evolution was awaiting the opportunity to generate these phyla. This implies preadaptive purpose and design in evolution. And Behe's concept of irreducible complexity at the microscopic level corroborates this implication.

The evidence for the Intelligence of a Creator is mounting. The universe had a discreet beginning and evolved according to plan. Humanity and every other biological species evolved according to plan. Biologically the logic of evolution is apparently contained in the logic of the genes. Evolution is the most complex ordering phenomenon ever discovered. At the level of individual species and classes it appears utterly systematic. And it is now time to explore the overall systematic nature – the master blueprint – of the processes at work.

---

1   Darwin mentions the woodpecker as an example of an exquisite coadaptation in *The Origin of Species* (New York: Gramercy Books, 1979), 114 . [This is a republication of the first edition of Darwin's great classic, which first appeared in 1859.]

2   M. Denton, *Evolution: A Theory in Crisis* (Bethesda, Md.: Adler & Adler, 1986), 202–7.

3   M. Behe, *Darwin's Black Box: The Biochemical Challenge to Evolution* (New York: The Free Press, 1996).

4   F. Crick, *Life Itself* (New York: Simon and Shuster, 1981).

5   See I. Prigogine and I. Stengers, *Order out of Chaos: Man's New Dialogue with Nature* (Toronto: Bantam Books), 1984; N. Eldredge, *Time Frames: The Rethinking of Darwinian Evolution and the Theory of Punctuated Equilibrium* (New York: Simon and Shuster, 1985) ; G. Nicolis and I. Prigogine, *Explaining Complexity: An Introduction* (New York: W.H. Freeman, 1987); and S. Kauffman, *The Origins of Order: Self-Organization and Selection in Evolution* (Oxford: Oxford University Press, 1993), and *At Home in the Universe, The Search for Laws of Self-Organization and Complexity* (Oxford: Oxford University Press, 1995).

Behe's approach to the mathematical field of complexity is to quote John Maynard Smith's quip that Kauffman practises "fact free science" (*Darwin's Black Box*, 156). He is correct in so far as we are given a lot of mathematics and very little chemistry in these discussions. From my point of view, self-ordering systems do represent something of a challenge. They appear to offer a theoretical basis for traditional Darwinist thought, even if the facts are scarce. Yet I still don't think that Darwinism can survive in its present form; the gradualism just doesn't work. Palaeontologists have already revolted: in particular, Eldredge and Gould's theory of punctuated equilibrium has abandoned gradual evolution. They maintain, instead, that the evolutionary event is concentrated in the speciation event. Thus, there exist long periods of stability or stasis, punctuated by short bursts of evolution. It is interesting to note that adaptive evolutionary events must also be concentrated in the speciation event. The attractiveness of punctuated equilibrium is that it is compatible with the fossil record. In the fossil record, we don't see a lot of evolution going on, which can be rather embarrassing for more traditional Darwinist advocates. While it is difficult to comprehend how random mutations could be so concentrated over short intervals of time, self-ordering saltations could, theoretically, save the day for at least a quite modified form of traditional Darwinist thought. If Behe is correct in his irreducible complexity arguments (and I believe he is), then Darwinists will have to embrace "fact-free" self-ordering systems, since they won't have anywhere else to go. And, with this in mind, I have concentrated in this book on Darwinism today as a self-ordering, rather than a gradual mutating system.

6 S. Gould, *Wonderful Life: The Burgess Shale and the Nature of History* (New York: W.W. Norton, 1989). Gould makes a powerful argument for this aspect of contingency throughout this book.

7 Interested readers will find the *Encyclopaedia Britannica* an excellent source of additional information on many of the particular cases outlined in the discussion which follows here.

8 V. Scheffer, *Spires of Form: Glimpses of Evolution* (Seattle: University of Washington Press, 1983). Scheffer discusses his finding the poorwill in a dormant state.

9 See A. Romer, *The Vertebrate Story* (Chicago: The University of Chicago Press, 1967), ch. 4, for a highly readable account of what is required for the transition onto land.

10 S. Gould, *Hen's Teeth & Horse's Toes* (New York: W.W. Norton, 1983), 182–4. Gould gives an account of the induction of teeth and the regression to a more primitive leg structure. "Chick epithelium had not only induced mouth mesenchyme to form dentin; it had also been able to generate enamel matrix proteins." (183)

11 Romer, *Vertebrate Story*, 226–8. Many accounts of the therapsids are available, but this seems to me a particularly good introduction for general readers.

12 See H. Jerison, *Evolution of the Brain and Intelligence* (New York: Academic Press, 1973).

13 Sex has caused endless problems for Darwinist thought. Interested readers can sample the divergence of opinions in R. Dawkins, *The Selfish Gene* (Oxford: Oxford University Press, 1976), and G. Williams, *Sex and Evolution* (Princeton: Princeton University Press, 1975). Williams all but gives up on trying to understand sex in terms of reductionist models of evolution.

14 G. Taylor, *The Great Evolution Mystery* (London: Secker & Warburg, 1983), 189–90.

15 Scheffer, *Spires of Form*.

16 R. Dawkins, *The Blind Watchmaker* (London: W.W. Norton, 1985), ch. 2.

17 Romer, *Vertebrate Story*, 153–5.

18 The absence of transitional forms is a perennial problem for Darwinists. The fish have left no transitional fossils in their conquest of the land as amphibians. In turn, the amphibians have left no hint as to how they evolved the amniotic egg so typical of the reptiles.

19 S. Gould, *The Panda's Thumb* (New York: W.W. Norton, 1980).

20 One of the ways out of evolutionary jumps is the notion of punctuated equilibria advocated by Eldredge and Gould. Their paper on the subject can be found as an appendix in N. Eldredge, *Time Frames: The Rethinking of Darwinian Evolution and the Theory of Punctuated Equilibrium* (New York: Simon and Shuster, 1985). I hasten to add that Eldredge and Gould are not 'saltationists,' though their theory poses immense problems in explaining large-scale adaptive evolution without saltation.

21 In contemporary science we often find terms of derision associated with unpopular

views. As noted earlier, "big bang" was originally a term of derision coined by Fred Hoyle. In a similar vein, Richard Goldschmidt's large-scale evolutionary jumps or 'hopeful monsters' was an object of scorn in Darwinist circles for many years. He challenged whoever would listen to explain a long list of adaptations by a series of gradual changes. This is reminiscent of Denton and Behe today. Goldschmidt was attacking the right problem, though he went too far on the genetic front. Evolution appears somehow directed and capable of great leaps of complexity. His analysis of the problems of evolution were quite prophetic. See R. Goldschmidt, *The Material Basis of Evolution* (New Haven: Yale University Press, 1940).

22 See P. Cloud, *Oasis in Space: Earth History from the Beginning* (New York: W.W. Norton & Company, 1988). Chapter 13 gives an excellent introduction to the beginning of metazoan life. One can also consult the *Encyclopaedia Britannica* for articles on the base of the Cambrian. And see M. McMenamin and D. McMenamin, *The Emergence of Animals: The Cambrian Breakthrough* (New York: Columbia University Press, 1990).

23 Cloud, *Oasis in Space*, 327.

24 Gould, *Wonderful Life,* is an excellent and highly readable commentary on the fauna of the Burgess Shale. Also, see S. Conway-Morris and H. Whittington, "The Animals of the Burgess Shale," *Scientific American,* July 1979 , 122–33. There is a brief overview in R. Leakey and R. Lewin, *The Sixth Extinction: Patterns of Life and the Future of Humankind* (New York: Doubleday, 1995), ch. 2. And see, as well, J. Levinton, "The Big Bang of Animal Evolution," *Scientific American,* November 1992.

25 "Some fifteen to twenty Burgess species cannot be allied with any known group, and should probably be classified as separate phyla." (Gould, *Wonderful Life*, 25.) Later work tends to indicate that Gould may have gone too far in his assessment of these fossils. Some of them are not as unique as he had originally believed: see Levinton, "Big Bang of Animal Evolution."

26 Stratigraphic terms can be quite daunting to the non-geologist, and I have tried to keep them to a minimum. The Precambrian is not a proper term in stratigraphy, but it is useful for general references to the time before the Cambrian period or, indeed, for all the time prior to the Cambrian. Palaeozoic refers to the ancient life of the Earth and we can think of it as roughly spanning the time from 600 million years to 225 million years before the present (or bp). The Mesozoic is the middle-life era and it stretches from 225 to 65 million years bp. The Cenozoic is the modern-life era and it stretches from 65 million years to the present. To make matters even more complicated, some geologists speak about the Quaternary period, to refer to the time when humankind existed. It is not an era, nor is it of much value as a period.

27 Behe, *Darwin's Black Box.*

CHAPTER 4

The Master Blueprint

In Chapter 3, I argued that every organism exhibits a state of near-perfect adaptation to its environment. This led to a search for evidence that evolution is an intelligently designed process that has systematically generated logically constructed organisms. Many examples were cited but the biological earthquake at the base of the Cambrian Period was presented as the most compelling and persuasive case.

In this biological earthquake the intellectual concept of incorporating a skeleton as an integral component of an organism's anatomy was brought to life simultaneously by four genetic saltations or leaps, that produced respectively brachiopods, arthropods, mollusks, and echinoderms – four of the most complex animal phyla in existence. In each instance the soft tissues of the organisms were massively 'retooled' so as to facilitate and exploit the skeleton. These four phyla had no access to ancestors from which to inherit the skeleton, and nowhere in the living world was there any genetic information about the new environmental conditions of increasing oxygen. The case implies design in a quite dramatic way.

Bolstered by this unusually persuasive evidence at the base of the Cambrian period we can explain the major cases of evolutionary convergence in the same manner: the camera-type eye in the mollusks and the vertebrates, the similar porpoise-type organisms in the reptiles and the mammals, two timber-wolf creatures in the marsupials and placentals, and so forth. We can then extrapolate all the way back to the near perfection of all species. This perfection in adaptation in each species was and is the result of a systematic genetic change at work. This raises questions about the relationship species have to each other and whether life itself is systematically organized. And this leads directly to a deeper exploration of biological classification in contemporary science.

AN INTRODUCTION TO BIOLOGICAL CLASSIFICATION

Estimates of the number of living species of all organisms range from 10 to 30 million. At least a million animal species and half a million plant species have already been described. The degree of biological diversity is even more astounding when one takes account of the extinct species. In all probability, somewhere in the region of one to three billion species did at one time or another exist on the Earth. In comparison to the most complex entities of the physical world, any given species represents a quantum leap in organizational sophistication and intricacy of design. Remarkably, all these magnificent creatures are related to each other.

A majority of biologists believe that there was only one original mother cell – an Eve, as it were, to all life. All living things use the same small repertoire of chemical elements. The major ones are carbon, hydrogen, nitrogen, oxygen, phosphorous, and sulphur. The minor ones are zinc, sodium, magnesium, iron, calcium, manganese, potassium, copper, selenium, and cobalt. All organisms have genetic information systems consisting of similar deoxyribonucleic acid (DNA) macro-molecules, composed of at least two million pure component molecules or building blocks. The action of cells is carried out by proteins and they are all coded for by the genes.

Proteins are all built from the same 20 fundamental building blocks. All living organisms possess ribosomes, which are organelles within the cell that manufacture proteins with the aid of genetic instructions. An extremely important group within the proteins is the enzymes. Enzymes act as catalysts to help chemical reactions along. The astonishing thing about them is that they are inordinately specific: they perform one task extremely well while they are near useless for anything else. This specificity of proteins and enzymes is shared by all living things. The element phosphorous also plays a vital role in the affairs of all living organisms, even though its geochemical abundance on the Earth is less than one percent. Phosphorous is essential in a great range of cell processes. It is required to build the DNA molecule, and indispensable in the energy affairs of all cells in the form of adenosine monophosphate (AMP), adenosine diphosphate (ADP), and adenosine triphosphate (ATP).

All life forms have the same type of molecules as genes and all genes can copy themselves, giving rise to the 'heredity' characteristic of living organisms. All cells manufacture their own proteins under instructions from the genes, and they all have batteries of highly specific enzymes. Phosphorous plays a highly critical role in the economy of all living cells. Taken together, all these similarities have convinced a majority of biologists today (and most of the wider scientific community) that all living organisms derive from some first or ancestral cell, which had all the similar characteristics to begin with.

It is staggering to think that all living things on Earth share one simple living cell as an ancestor. And such a thought raises two related and almost equally staggering questions. The first involves accounting for the origin of the first or ancestral living cell. I will be devoting my full attention to this issue in the final two chapters of this book.

The second almost equally staggering question involves coming to terms with the extravagant evolutionary potential of the first or ancestral cell, as displayed by the stupendous diversity of living things today and throughout geological history. This points more specifically to the principles or system of classification that contemporary science has adopted (or perhaps 'discovered' is the better word), to bring some order to the stupendous diversity of living things. And this is the more exact subject that I am exploring in this chapter.

THE CLASSIFICATION SYSTEM

When we speak of the wonders of the world, evolution sits isolated in a class all of its own. It would still be a marvel if that first cell, the Eve of life, had only given rise to a billion cells of similar complexity. But large-scale or 'macro-evolution' is the process that really inspires awe. In this case there is a substantial increment in the level of organization between the parent and the sibling species.

The difference in organization of a bacterium and a nuclear cell has been compared to that of a bicycle and a jet airliner. In turn multicellular organisms are themselves a quantum leap in complexity over single-celled organisms. Of all the recorded evolutionary achievements, that which culminates in the human brain is arguably the most profound. Human self-consciousness is a profound saltation, perhaps equalling the jump from the inanimate to the animate. Among all of the billion organisms that do and did exist one solitary species, humanity, is both intelligent and self-conscious. Evolution is the wondrous process whereby life has literally pulled itself up by its own bootlaces to ever-increasingly elaborate levels of organization until, finally, life knows that it exists.

With 10 to 20 million living species of organisms and a billion extinct, biology is confronted with an overwhelming quantity of data. A rigorous classification system is required to cope with this volume of information. At the very least, one would obviously need a catalogue structure of some sort. When confronted with a new discovery one has to find a place for it in the existing classification. Questions such as how does one name it, where does one place it and why, will inevitably arise. Thus all classification systems over time become imbued with theory. Inevitably, the natural order in the world being classified becomes the subject of hypotheses and principles. If evolution generated organisms indiscriminately, then the classification systems constructed would ultimately reflect this randomness. The construction and qualification for each category would be arbitrary and subjective. An alphabetical system similar to the telephone directory could be set up. An arbitrarily assigned name would then determine the organism's place in the classification. In this system the organism's position in the classification would carry no significance.

The revealing feature about life's great diversity is that it is not random at all. Biologists have constructed a hierarchical system that has the shape of a pyramid and they are almost unanimous that the major divisions and categories in the present system indicate real differences in the living world. If a new classification system were to be set up, all the major divisions presently recognized would inevitably emerge. The biological classification system ranks amongst the great intellectual achievements of all time. There is no *a priori* reason why the diversity of life on Earth could be sensibly classified in a highly systematic way. That the human mind can impose order on such diversity requires an explanation. The ability to build an abstract classification system to house all of life is reminiscent of the ability of physics to use abstract mathematics and symmetry to explain the universe.

The biological classification system arranges organisms into groups on the basis of their similarities and relationships. It has the logic of a pyramid. The greatest common denominator occurs at the apex of the pyramid. Each descending level is more specific until at the bottom an organism is exactly specified. Most human filing systems have a hierarchical nature. Libraries are prime candidates but in reality any efficient office has some form of hierarchical classification system. In a library one goes from non-fiction to science to chemistry to the specific text. Each sub-classification is supposed to be contained fully within the classification above. Nearly all such classification systems have halfway entries where it is not clear which of a number of options ought to be chosen. Whether we call these overlaps or miscellaneous items, they are a constant feature of classifications devised for human affairs.

Overlaps arise because the progression of human knowledge has not been absolutely systematic. Human knowledge has grown erratically and it has deep roots in history. From age to age our knowledge has evolved and it bears the influence and stamp of previous generations. Western philosophy is founded on ancient Greek wisdom (which in turn owed a lot to the ancient wisdom of Asia). Mathematics bears the influence of Pythagoras and Euclid, while science bears the influence of Aristotle. The roots of many English words can be traced back to their Latin and Greek counterparts. Every historical period has had its influence on the store of human knowledge, some greater than others. Modern knowledge is the product of an evolutionary process with multiple links to its antecedents in history.

By and large, the biological classification system is relatively free of overlapping categories. In the higher ranks of the system there is an absence of ambiguity. To give a name to an organism we work our way down this rigid hierarchical system and assign a binomial name using the genus and species in question. Humans, for example, are in the animal kingdom, the chordate phylum, the mammalian class, the primate order, the hominid family, the Homo genus, and the sapiens species. The binomial nomenclature uses the capitalized genus and the lower-cased species together, and it must be Latin or Latin-sounding (thus the scientific name for humans is *Homo sapiens* and so forth).

This approach to classification, without its subsequent refinements beyond the categories of class, order, and genus, was first devised and consistently used by the Swedish naturalist Linnaeus. Linnaeus assumed that he was simply unravelling the plan of creation, and that the order of the biological classification system ultimately derived from the Creator's having designed every living organism. Herbert Wendt tells us that the young Linnaeus "suddenly saw nature not as a chaotic mass of wonders and puzzles, but as an orderly hierarchy, disposed and organized by Divine providence ... Every phenomenon, rock, herb, and tree, fish, bird, and quadruped, and Man also, was firmly rooted in its proper place."[1] This explicit underlying religious philosophy has of course been abandoned by modern biologists, but the hierarchical classification system that Linnaeus began has continued to this day.

During the early part of the nineteenth century taxonomists arranged organisms into 'natural' groups. In this fashion the biological classification system was gradually expanded and built up. All the songbirds, for example, were put together into one major group, which in its turn was part of the class of animals we know as birds. The birds in turn belong to the vertebrates, which in turn belong to the animal kingdom. Biologists achieved success in using taxonomic groups defined by naturally occurring affinities between organisms, and this accomplishment implies some underlying fundamental order to life. In chemistry we have an analogue in Mendeleev's periodic table. All the elements that make up the world were grouped together by weight and chemical properties. The order underlying the periodic table was such that chemists were able to predict the existence of elements as yet undiscovered. They were also able to guess the physical and chemical properties of these unknown elements. A pattern in any classification system implies a reason, a cause, and an explanation.

The work of the empirical taxonomists of the nineteenth century showed that the living world could be sensibly classified into a hierarchical system. Essentially, the ranks of kingdom, phylum, class, order, family, genus, and species remain intact today. At the apex of the system is the characteristic of DNA or ribonucleic acid (RNA) and reproduction. Anything that has DNA and can reproduce itself is a living organism and it must have a place in the classification system. We generally recognize five kingdoms, four of which are well known and unambiguous: animals, plants, fungi, and bacteria. The fifth tends to be less clearly defined and is variously known as the protists or proctoctista. Within these kingdoms there are just over 90 phyla recognized at present. The term phylum is generally not as well-known as the other terms in the classification system. Unfortunately this bears no relationship whatsoever to its importance. The phylum represents the basic level of anatomical organization within each kingdom. After the level of phylum, the number of representatives of each successive rank increase quite rapidly. The species, which is the lowest category in the classification system, may have as many as 30 million individual representatives.

RECENT DEBATES ABOUT THE SYSTEM

Initially the only theoretical underpinning for this order in the biological world was a belief in the God-given order of the universe. Many contemporary scientists seem surprised at how easily their more remote predecessors integrated a belief in God with the natural order and philosophy of science. When Darwin formulated his theory of evolution he interpreted the natural hierarchy in terms of descendence. Natural groupings in the hierarchy existed because the members of these groups had descended from a common ancestor. But a provocative feature of the Darwinist approach to biological taxonomy (or the principles of biological classification) is that it had little or no impact on the established classification system. Even though the theoretical understanding of organic diversity had changed quite dramatically, there was no need to rearrange everything from scratch. The implication here is that the broad levels of order in the classification system established by the empirical taxonomists constitute a genuine scientific phenomenon. They reflect the 'natural' order of the biological world.

A fundamental level of biological order is revealed in the structural consistency of the hierarchical classification of living things. The reliability, distinctiveness, and isolation of each rank or category in the taxonomy improves as we go higher up the pyramid. The species, subspecies, and populations, are subject to endless research and revision. An immense amount of evolutionary research has been done at the level of the species and the variations within species and populations. Thankfully, we need not concern ourselves with evolution at this level. All the momentous or macro-evolutionary events involve taxa higher than the species. At the level of genus we can have more confidence, but it is still prudent not to seek out the more exotic genus for discussion. At the level of the family, by and large, we have reached a level of considerable confidence. Here there is usually an unambiguous gap between the family in question and even the closest other family. Above the rank of family there is an unambiguous discontinuity between the taxon and any other taxon of the same rank. Most higher taxa are defined by an inclusion principle. If a species has most of the appropriate characteristics for a particular taxon, it is placed in this taxon.

Since the time of Darwin all of biology has been deeply influenced by explicitly 'evolutionary' thinking and theory. Naturally the taxonomy of living things has also felt this influence. Almost all biologists today recognize biological evolution as a genuine natural phenomenon. It is generally accepted that the lineage of all living things stretches back in time through a series of taxonomically different ancestors to the first living thing. Darwin's explanation of this ancestry drew on the concept of natural selection, operating on inherent variations found in individuals and leading gradually to the generation of new species. The modern synthesis explains the inherent variations that are acted upon by natural selection in terms of random genetic mutations. And Darwin was absolutely emphatic that there could be no leaps or saltations allowed. As the contemporary Darwinist philosopher Daniel Dennett has explained: "Even before Darwin, the received wisdom of biologists was, as Linnaeus said in his classic work of taxonomy (1751), *"Natura non facit saltus"* – nature does not make leaps – and this was one maxim that Darwin didn't just leave untouched; he provided enormous support for it."[2] Darwin committed himself to the philosophy of gradualism so deeply ingrained in geology today: "The present is the key to the past." Slow, steady, continuous processes, on this view lead to an accumulation of gradual, but inexorable, change. Inevitably, there must be links between all descendants and ancestors.

As a result of this particular Darwinian influence on interpretation, as little as 20 years ago it was widely thought that the traditional biological classification system had begun to generate artificial results. There were whole classes of organisms sitting in neat isolated groups in the system. Some of these groups should have been indicating greater levels of affinity to some classes than others. Yet known relationships of this sort were plainly not materializing, and the isolation of each major rank in the classification system was construed as an artifact of the methods of classification rather than a reflection of any biological reality. It was a fairly widespread belief that fish were closer to the amphibians than they were to the reptiles. The fish were in turn closer to the reptiles than to the birds or the mammals. This is the unambiguous evolutionary sequence. That the classification system failed to show this relationship was seen as evidence that it was producing spurious indications of isolation.

The molecular biologist Michael Denton, however, has more recently shown that the isolation of the ranks in the system is not a quirk of classification.[3] The findings of molecular biology support all the key features of the traditional hierarchical classification system, including the isolation of individual higher ranks. The classification system *is* reflecting innate biological features, rather than any mere artifact of methodology.

The first attempts to compare the closeness of organisms at the molecular level or with chemical analysis employed blood serum tests.[4] These tests were used to determine closeness between the proteins of different organisms. The blood serum examinations tended to give results that were interpreted as entirely supporting the natural selection model of evolution. Over the last two decades technology has been developed to compare the DNA or the protein composition directly. This new technology allows us to determine the exact composition of the proteins. The amino acid sequence of a protein that is used by two dissimilar organisms can be compared and the differences in the two chains quantified.

All aerobic organisms, for example, need to handle oxygen and therefore must have the cytochrome enzyme. It has been found that the same type of protein in different species has differences in the sequences of amino acids that make up the protein, and these differences are brought about by substituting one amino acid for a similar but different amino acid. There is substitution in the amino acid sequence. The sequences in the same type of proteins in closely related species are very closely related, with only small percentage changes due to substitution. In comparison, the differences in the amino acid sequence in dissimilar organisms is always greater. There is consistently more substitution in distantly related species than in closely related species, and these differences in the amino acid sequences can be quantified.

All the major ranks in the hierarchical classification system identified by large-scale anatomical features or macroscopic criteria can be identified by the differences in amino acid sequences in proteins. When the microscopic observations confirm the macroscopic observations there is validation that the hierarchy of the classification of life is in itself a major feature of life. Molecular biology also indicates that all members of one rank are equally representative of that rank. There is no member more typical of the rank than another. This means that both the proteins and the classification system fail to pick out the immediate ancestry of organisms. Moreover, no intermediates exist whatsoever. Each rank in the taxonomy is innately isolated from every other rank. Because the links are missing, the ancestry that must of necessity have once existed has now disappeared completely.

The evolutionary sequence of fish, amphibians, reptiles, birds, and mammals is well-established. In terms of historical ancestry, birds and mammals ought to be more distant from the fish than are amphibians. But this is apparently not the case. Amphibians and reptiles are no nearer to fish than are mammals and birds. Each taxon is independent of all other taxa of the same level. Lower ranks within a given taxon are closer to each other than to any other outside rank. This means that lower ranks are fully contained within the taxon above. No ambiguity exists. It also implies that each rank is fundamental in nature, since no distinction between members of the same rank can be made.

This confirmation of the hierarchical classification of all living things – based on relating visible anatomical features with the features of living cell chemistry – would seem to be rather momentous. It implies that biologists, while attempting to impose their own innate intelligence on the diversity of the living world via the classification system, have uncovered instead a natural hierarchical order in life. Hierarchical systems deal with information flow and decision-making: they are the artifacts of intelligent design. Most human societies and organizations exhibit hierarchical features.[5] Military organizations, with their field marshall, a handful of generals, and ever-increasing numbers of colonels, captains, lieutenants, NCOs and a mass of individual soldiers, are unusually rigid examples. Business organizations, while maintaining the hierarchical structure, allow for far more autonomy at each of the individual ranks. All hierarchies are, nonetheless, intelligently designed structures that are meant to control restricted flows of information between ranks, of one sort or another. Our computer directories exhibit this feature. So, too, do our libraries and our offices.

Modern research is rapidly reducing the rationality of biology to the logic of the information in the genes. The biological classification system has been confirmed at the level of protein composition. But proteins and protein composition are under the control of the genes. Hence, the confirmation at the level of protein composition equates to confirmation at the level of genetic information. Every major taxon or category in the classification system is confirmed by protein analysis. Thus each category represents a discrete level of genetic organization. And thus the natural hierarchy of biological life that so closely parallels human hierarchical arrangements for information flow and decision-making is composed of natural levels of information. What biologists have discovered, as it were, is nature's information-flow system or 'master genetic blueprint.'

From the first living cell onwards evolution is the craftsman that has generated all other living things. In the same sense evolution has generated all the features of life's hierarchical arrangement. But all evolution is driven by the genes irrespective of how one interprets the mechanics of the process: hence the hierarchy is genetic in nature. Such an arrangement is not only consistent with the concept of evolution as an intelligently designed process that produces intelligent results: it almost demands such a concept. Hierarchical information-flow systems are not the artifacts of spontaneous processes, but the hallmarks of intelligent design and organization. We have just caught a glimpse of the Creator at work.

REDUCTIONISM AND THE CLASSIFICATION SYSTEM

It seems to me that bringing the evidence of palaeontology to bear on the biological classification system has some additional and related implications for traditional Darwinist thought. To start with, Darwin's nineteenth-century prediction was for evolution to proceed in a steady and gradual fashion, via large numbers of linked species:

> The main cause, however, of innumerable intermediate links not now occurring everywhere throughout nature depends on the very process of natural selection, through which new varieties continually take the places of and exterminate their parent-forms. But just in proportion as this process of extermination has acted on an enormous scale, so must the number of intermediate varieties, which have formerly existed on the earth be truly enormous.[6]

A theory predicting steady gradualism, in other words, cannot tolerate jumps or leaps: this means that there must be intermediates or links between all related categories or taxa in the biological classification system. Yet the evidence from palaeontology and biology together is that there exist virtually no links at all between the higher taxa! The one good link that does exist – the extinct ancient bird Archaeopteryx – ultimately presents more problems for natural selection than it solves. And one link is altogether inadequate in any case. Literally thousands of links are required and they simply do not exist. The higher taxa are islands unto themselves. Every order of biology is utterly isolated from all other orders. Every class is utterly isolated from every other class in biology. Inordinate numbers of links are missing.

Similarly, the four phyla at the base of the Cambrian period can only be explained by means of massive genetic jumps. This alone confounds the traditional Darwinian prediction. The notion that chunks of the organization of highly complex organisms can be altered successfully to higher levels of complexity by contingent processes cannot be sustained. The present-day Darwinist philosopher Dennett says it quite eloquently:

> Large leaps sideways *in a fitness landscape* will almost never be to your benefit; wherever you currently find yourself, you are where you are because this has been a good region of Design Space for your ancestors – you are near the top of some peak or other in space – so, the bigger the step you take (jumping randomly, of course), the more likely you are to jump off a cliff ...[7]

On top of this problem there is the unfortunate observation that most fossil species show virtually no tendency to evolve at all. The correlation of different sequences of rocks is the study of stratigraphy. The very best tool available for this correlation is the fossils contained in the sedimentary rocks. The success of stratigraphy using fossils is based on the fact that one can recognize the designated type-fossil for a formation at different locations. If all species were evolving away steadily then this drift would reduce our chances of recognizing and identifying the fossil in different locations.[8] If evolutionary drift were a common feature, then the fossils in the rocks would be in a state of continuous change, and extreme difficulties would be encountered in determining where a given fossil fitted into the sequence. Fossil-based stratigraphy under these conditions would be chaotic in the extreme. But in fact it does work. Fossil-based stratigraphy is the finest tool in the geological arsenal for correlating different rock types. Palaeontologists do not spend their working lives fretting about the degree of change a species may have undergone. They work on the assumption that the species will run true to type and the stratigraphical results in the field are excellent.

There is no substitute for evidence and the success of stratigraphy provides some considerable assurance that fossil species did little evolving on the job. What we tend to find is that a fossil appears at a certain horizon of rocks and then goes out at a certain higher horizon. The fossil appears abruptly and then later the same fossil disappears fairly abruptly: in between, it is the same species of fossil. The historical record shows that most evolutionary events, whether major or minor, occurred over very short periods of time, followed by long periods of stability.

Palaeontologists are thus strongly prompted to conclude that all of the evolutionary event is concentrated in the circumstance of generating a new species. This implies that most evolution proceeds by genetic jumps from species to species. Major evolutionary events would of necessity require considerable change over small periods of time – and fairly substantial jumps in the process. The field evidence conforms rather closely with the isolation of each major rank in the biological classification system. In order to generate the isolation we have to leave very few intermediate fossils. In order to leave very few fossils the genetic changes must consist of fairly rapid jumps. This is what the field evidence implies, and it is not easy to reconcile with Darwin's nineteenth-century predictions.

Darwinist thought has also advanced the concept of common ancestry to explain the order in the biological classification system. And this does make sense since heredity is a genetic function. We do, however, have to be quite clear as to which ancestor we are talking about. Imagine, for example, that species A has evolved into a new genus. Two new species, B and C, evolve from A. Two more species, D and E, evolve from C. It is clear that D and E have two common ancestors in C and A. But the ancestor of B is A: and therefore the common ancestry of the entire genus goes back to A. The inheritance of the original genetic distinguishing trait is from A for the entire genus.

This general reduction back to the first ancestor holds for all the higher taxonomic ranks in the classification system.[9] If this were not the case then it would be possible to distinguish 'closeness' in each rank. A member of each rank would not be equally representative of that rank as any other member. The most recent members would be 'closer' to more recent members than to the most ancient members. As discussed earlier, molecular biology contradicts this notion. Denton has shown that every member of a rank is equally representative of that rank: when we speak of the common ancestry of the classification system we really mean the first organism that appears with a particular anatomical blueprint. The common ancestry of the vertebrates goes all the way back to the first vertebrate, which probably evolved in the Ordovician period between 435 and 500 million years ago. And on this evidence it makes just as much sense to talk of 'common design' as 'common ancestor.'

The ancestry that is preserved is always the highest common rank above the level at which the evolutionary event has occurred. If a new class is evolved then the phylum is the ancestral rank preserved. If a new order is evolved then the class is the ancestral rank preserved. This is what generates the isolation of the higher ranks. In effect, all lower ancestral affinities between a parent species and a new species are eliminated, and this is the evolutionary pattern as represented by the biological classification system.

To spin the argument out, every organism that lived or is living has existed as a species: so it must be closer to members of its own immediate genus than species belonging to other genera. Major taxonomic change can only occur at the level of individuals which are themselves members of the species. The bewildering fact is that major evolutionary change wipes out this closeness at the levels of the lower taxa. The classes fish, amphibian, reptile, bird, and mammal all exhibit this phenomenon. We know that this is the evolutionary sequence. Yet we cannot show any parental affinities between the classes. The fish are not closer to the amphibians than they are to the reptiles. In turn they are not closer to the reptiles than they are to the birds or mammals. And this implies that all the lower ancestral affinities have been overwritten or eliminated.

In the end we have a quite radical departure from what was originally intended by the principle of ordering through ancestry. A process that eliminates all traces of lower ancestral affinities is operating in a highly systematic fashion. And how systematic can a self-ordering process based on contingency be? Considering the sheer immensity of geological time, five kingdoms and 90-odd phyla add up to remarkably few basic blueprints of life. It is this feature that lies at the heart of the order of the classification system. That there are so few phyla speaks eloquently for the notion that there exists a systematic constraint on anatomical layouts. The implication is that the phyla are the preferred or even 'innate' designs for life.

In the traditional Darwinian reductionist paradigm it is possible, if most unlikely, that the 90-odd phyla in existence are exhaustive. Perhaps, given the environmental constraints on a living organism, no other fundamental layout will work. In essence this amounts to contingency searching for and exhausting all possibilities. And this may explain why a number of phyla-like arrangements in the Burgess Shale of British Columbia never ultimately materialized into actual phyla. Yet this explanation fails to account for the complete absence of evolutionary attempts at the level of phyla over the 530-million-year period after the Burgess Shale. If contingency can be creative over 30 times, why not once more?

In fact, conservation of this sort is not restricted to the level of phyla. It is actually rampant in biology. The crocodiles and the marine turtles have done little or nothing in evolutionary design for millions of years. Insects display a similar resistance to fundamental change. We also have what are known as living fossils. Didelphis, the American possum, is still the same after 75 million years. Sphenodon is a lizard-like reptile confined to New Zealand, and it has existed unchanged for 150 million years. Limulus, the horseshoe crab, has stuck with its basic design for 175 million years. The brachiopod, Lingula, has not changed for 400 million years. While these creatures generate slightly different species, it appears that a fundamental design is conserved. Many types of bacteria have also remained unchanged for billions of years. The implication from these examples is that the evolutionary process tends to conserve 'good designs.' And this in itself speaks of some highly systematic phenomenon at work. Of course the ultimate question is whether the good designs flow systematically from predetermined logical configurations of information in the genes, or merely from contingent 'accidents' of natural history. And my ultimate argument here is that the hierarchical nature of biology suggests that the operation of the genes is itself organized hierarchically.

EVOLUTION AS A SYSTEMATIC AND PREDETERMINED PROCESS

I want to end my work here, on the master blueprint, by pursuing the general argument about the systematic nature of evolution a few more steps. And the first of these steps returns to the case where the same fundamental 'good design' is derived independently by different ancestors. In the last chapter, for instance, I discussed how the same type of wolf has been generated by both marsupials and placentals. This convergence of evolution implies preference in the evolutionary process. When genes are mutating away, they have to know where to stop. When two independent lines arrive at the same 'stop,' there has to be some logical control.

Similarly, such evolutionary sagas as those of the therapsids, who gave rise to mammals on their way to extinction, of all the ancestral birds with a toothed jaw who gave rise to descendants with beaks, and of the phenomenal development of the brain that led to modern humanity, all point to some highly systematic process at work. Moreover, what most distinguishes this highly systematic evolutionary process, as it is recorded in the fossil record, is its dramatic success. Whatever else, the fossil record is a testimony of prodigious evolutionary achievement. Put another way, just where are the failures? If many were called and few selected, then the many who were passed over must have left some trace. Yet it is simply not possible to compile endless lists of failed prototypes of phyla, classes, and orders from the fossil record. And what else can this imply if it does not imply that failures are few and far between?

In fact, it seems that there is only one analogous phenomenon to evolution – the growth of a new creature in embryology. There are literally billions of human beings living on the face of our planet today: yet each one started out as a single cell. The embryological phenomenon of a single cell generating multicellular complex organisms points to a consummately successful and systematic biological mechanism at work. And so does the unequivocal success of evolution in generating new biological classes and orders and families. Both processes are a phenomena of biological growth. Embryology 'grows' a new organism under the direction of the genes. Evolution grows new genes under the direction of genes that already exist. To me, the most objective view is to accept the evidence as it is. The process of biological evolution must be both the most complex and the most systematic ordering system science has ever uncovered.

Ever since its origin more than 3.5 billion years ago, the phenomenon of biological life has persisted, without interruption, down to the present. While life as a whole continues without any break or discontinuity, the individual cells of life are in a state of constant change. It is in the nature of every cell to divide and create two identical daughter cells. Once a state of equilibrium is reached, an old cell must die for every new cell that is created. When we factor geological time into the equation, it becomes clear that the number of cells which have ever existed is altogether astronomical. And then it becomes an extraordinary observation that living things have suffered no loss of vitality, or no gradual degeneration into chaos.

Our own slight human experience shows how when copies of a template are themselves copied to any significant degree, errors invariably set in. Nowadays, for instance, we are all familiar with copying computer programs in our own electronic communication machines. Imagine that we have an extremely detailed and complex program to be copied. We make the first copy and use the verify function to eradicate any major error (our natural selection, as it were, at work). We make the second copy from the first copy and verify again. Then a third copy is made from the second, and on and on. No matter what we do, errors will creep into the copies, and these errors will be passed on to the next copy. By the time we have billions of copies (if we were so foolish as to make so many), the program will be unworkable. The source of much of the error lies in the physical medium in which the copying is taking place. Our majestic human technology is incapable of devising a fool-proof method of repeated copying under controlled conditions. Yet biological life existed in a hostile environment and made perfectly useable copies of itself and its offspring – for more than 3.5 billion years.

The ancestral cell to all life appeared on this Earth armed with a copying technology infinitely more accurate than anything humankind can devise – at present and perhaps forever. The actual copying process is physical in nature. The DNA double helix is pulled apart into two single strands, and each strand is copied every time a cell duplicates. Why life's copying system has not degenerated into complete chaos before now is an infinite mystery. No matter how accurate the system is, errors must crop up on a regular basis because the copying is physical in nature. Natural selection can take care of lethal errors. But how can it deal with 'neutral' errors, inherent in the nature of the copying process itself?

In fact, geneticists today do talk about neutral mutations, pseudo-genes, and junk DNA. About 90 percent of genetic material is thought to be junk DNA. Of course 90 percent seems like a lot, but it is surprisingly small for the length of geological time the copying process has been in operation. And we are obliged to return to geological time as our reference here, since evolution has occurred in geological time. If there was only one ancestral cell, as the mainstream of contemporary scientific opinion agrees there must have been, we could not rejuvenate the copying system of life. It was set with the origin of life and it has had to continue uninterrupted for over 3.5 billion years. Suppose we take up a point of departure at the emergence of the nuclear cell, about 1.5 billion years ago. Using a simple arithmetic estimation, 90 percent junk DNA today implies that neutral errors are accumulating in the genome at the rate of 1/50-millionth of one percent of the total genome each year. This level of accuracy is simply fantastic: one might even be excused for describing it as miraculous.

No physical process could produce this level of accuracy unless there was some correction mechanism built into the system.[10] But a correction mechanism can only be explained through design: What would an unknowing process actually correct for? If there exists a correcting mechanism in the genes, then we have great difficulty explaining evolution in the first place. Evolution must generate changes in the genes during the copying stage in order to generate new organisms. If these changes are being corrected, how can evolution proceed? But evolution did proceed and therein lies the problem. Useful genetic changes, in the form of new species, accumulated at a rate that is within an order of magnitude of the neutral genetic changes. It appears that the useful evolutionary changes have been permitted to occur. Biological organisms, that is to say, have been *designed* to evolve.[11]

Once again we confront the evidence of preadaptation. No individual organism has a requirement for the accuracy of the genetic copying system. The system could easily have been an order of magnitude less accurate and it would have served the purposes of the initial nuclear-celled organisms effectively. In fact, it would have allowed the descendants of the initial organism to carry on for well over 100 million years. This amount of time is, of course, in excess of the immediate needs of any organism. Yet evolution on the Darwinist model can only take place with individual organisms. Natural selection can only select for the immediate benefit of an individual. And it would be singularly coincidental if natural selection happened to hone the copying process in individual organisms to such a degree that the survival of life itself resulted as a by-product.

Alternatively, one can interpret the accuracy of the genetic copying process as an adaptation designed to ensure the survival of life over such immense periods as the 1.5 billion years since the emergence of the nuclear cell. And, however you look at it, it is indeed an awesome Mind that is capable of forward planning over stretches of time that defy our human imagination.

In the end, we now have four lines of evidence which suggest that biological evolution is the product of systematic growth within the genes:

(1) The systematic hierarchical classification of biology provides some compelling evidence of a methodical process at work.

(2) At a more general level, the survival of life for billions of years, and its ability to evolve, are most easily reconciled with a hierarchically controlled genetic system that enjoys extremely high degrees of accuracy when copying itself.

(3) On a much more specific level, every species appears perfectly adapted to its environment. The evolutionary process shows logical problem-solving and such extraordinary convergences as the timber wolf in the marsupials and the vertebrate eye in the mollusks. It also shows four simultaneous genetic leaps in response to changing oxygen levels, resulting in the four complex phyla that exploded onto the base of the Cambrian period.

(4) We can only marvel at the stupendous evolutionary history of the brain. Four vertebrate classes are involved. The ancient mammals developed far more brainpower than the lower vertebrates, and the modern mammals developed far more brainpower again. Within the mammals, the primates accelerated the trend. Finally, the hominid brain grew as never before in biological history and ultimately brought forth self-conscious intelligent human beings.

A FINAL SUMMING-UP (AND LOOKING AHEAD)

Biological evolution is the most complex ordering process known to humankind. What I have tried to demonstrate in this chapter is that it is also absolutely and utterly systematic.

The phenomenon of life started out as one single type of bacterial cell. Over a period of more than 3.5 billion years, biological evolution has generated in the order of one to three billion species, ranging in complexity from bacteria to modern humanity. There are no graveyards of failed prototypes in the fossil record: biological evolution is so successful a phenomenon that it must be considered a characteristic of life over geological time. The ability of life to survive unthinkable lengths of time while constantly copying genes for new organisms, while at the same time changing these genes through evolution, calls for some systematic process of change in the genes.

In its wake, the evolutionary process has left the biological classification system. The system is a methodical hierarchy of organization. Each higher category or rank is isolated. This isolation of ranks can be verified independently by protein analysis, which confirms that the order of the classification system is a natural hierarchy. It also signals that this order is genetically based. The logic of biology reduces to the logic of the information in the genes.

The hierarchy of biological classification is the information-flow system and master genetic blueprint of life. Hierarchical ordering of information-flow systems is a hallmark of intelligence. All this implies again that evolution is an intelligently designed process. And we can now link the unambiguous generation of human intelligence, the near-perfect adaptation of organisms signifying intelligent design, and the natural hierarchical order signifying a master genetic blueprint of life. The Creator of the universe has left a broad trail for us to follow. The trail leads back to the first cell – the Eve of all living things – and to the absolutely fundamental question of the origin of life itself.

1   H. Wendt, *In Search of Adam: The Story of Man's Quest for the Truth about His Earliest Ancestors* (Boston: Houghton Mifflin Company, 1956), 29–30.

2   D. Dennett, *Darwin's Dangerous Idea: Evolution and the Meaning of Life* (New York: Simon and Shuster, 1995), 288.

3   M. Denton, *Evolution: A Theory in Crisis* (Bethesda, Md.: Adler and Adler, 1986), esp. ch. 12. For a related discussion on hierarchies in nature, see A. Koestler and J. Smythies, eds., *Beyond Reductionism – The Alpbach Symposium* (London: Hutchinson, 1971).

Denton's work is essential reading for anybody looking for fresh perspectives on the great debate about evolution. The hierarchy in biology has generated considerable controversy. What exactly do the higher taxa represent? Goldschmidt maintained that the phylum type was produced first and that it subsequently separated into class, order, genus, etc. This is too simplistic, but it does introduce the central challenge: namely, how does speciation within a given phylum lead to a new phylum, or what is the nature of macro-evolution? Do the higher taxa have any real meaning in the world of biology, or are they just artifacts of the classification system? Denton appears to have decided the issue. If the higher taxa can be identified by molecular biology, then they must be 'real' scientific phenomena.

4   See Sir G. DeBeer, *Atlas of Evolution* (London: Nelson, 1964).

5   See A. Koestler, *Janus: A Summing Up* (London: Hutchinson, 1978) and *The Ghost in the Machine* (London: Arkana, 1989). Koestler has tried to develop a general theory of hierarchy. The essential idea is that each rank operates in a dual fashion. As it looks up the hierarchy the lower rank is an integral part and behaves that way, but as it looks down the hierarchy the rank becomes an autonomous whole.

6   C. Darwin, *The Origin of Species* (New York: Gramercy Books, 197), 291–2.

7   Dennett, *Darwin's Dangerous Idea*, 288.

8   N. Eldredge, *Time Frames: The Rethinking of Darwinian Evolution and the Theory of Punctuated Equilibrium* (New York: Simon and Shuster, 1985). As mentioned in a previous note, Eldredge and Gould have explained the apparent absence of gradual evolution in the fossil record in terms of rapid bursts of evolution during the speciation event, followed by long periods of stability or stasis.

9   In this sense, Goldschmidt was correct. He maintained that the phylum came first and then the class and then the order, etc. At the same time, a phylum type does not exist in isolation: the first phylum had to be represented by a species in a genus, which in turn belonged to an order, which in turn belonged to a class. R. Goldschmidt, *The Material Basis of Evolution* (New Haven: Yale University Press, 1940).

10 Molecular biologists already believe that they have identified one of these correction mechanisms in the form of DNA polymerase – an extremely complex enzyme vital to replication in bacteria and also, apparently, capable of correcting errors.

11 It has certainly not been my intention in writing this book to theorize on the mechanics of 'directed evolution.' That would constitute a separate (and much different) study in its own right. But drawing eclectically on Goldschmidt, Koestler, Denton, and the accuracy problem in the copying of genetic material, one might suggest some broad outlines for a model.

The accuracy of the evolutionary process has to be driven by hierarchical corrections. Each higher rank permits a limited amount of variation in the rank below it. As we ascend the hierarchy, the stability of the genetic configuration becomes more stable. The kingdom would represent an utterly stable configuration. Immediately below that, the phylum represents a highly stable configuration.

The process first determines the configuration of the phyla and each configuration is inherently stable. In animal history, this stage corresponds to the base of the Cambrian. All the stable phyla were generated during this period with a number of quasi-stable forms as represented by the Burgess Shale. Once formed, the phylum becomes locked in, and no new evolutionary innovation occurs. This is why the great extinctions, in particular the extinction of the Permo-Triassic boundary, failed to produce new phyla. Once the phylum is in place, its configuration permits the next rank in the hierarchy, the class, to evolve to its full potential. Once a class is established its stability, in turn, permits a range of evolution at the level of the order, and so on.

The fossil record bears this sequence out: phyla finish their evolution first, then the classes, and then the orders, etc. In the great extinction at the Permo-Triassic boundary, evolution generated a whole host of new lower ranks. Finally, the process must become specific at the level of the genus and the species, and it was at this stage that the human species was permitted to evolve. Embryology lends some support to an, of course, rather speculative model of this sort. Following the old recapitulation theory, one can argue that the embryo develops under hierarchical guidance, where the phyla-type instructions come in before the class, etc. A model of this sort would also be similar to the model for the evolution of the universe: the strict hierarchical stabilities replace the cosmic coincidences in the role of permitting evolution to generate complexity.

CHAPTER 5

The Genesis of Life

The trail linking human intelligence through biological evolution to the proposed Creator of the universe logically leads back to the genesis of life on Earth. When all is said and done, there are two opposing hypotheses on the origin of life today. In the reductionist view of traditional Darwinist philosophy, life is altogether natural. It can be explained completely by the laws and properties governing matter and the material universe. Life's origins in this sense are 'intra-universal.' In the view of traditional monotheistic philosophy, life cannot be altogether explained naturally. In the end, the laws and properties of the matter contained in the universe are so inadequate in explaining life that they demand the existence of some intelligent Force outside the universe. Life's origins in this sense are 'extra-universal.'

In the world of science, the experiment is king. No biochemist has ever synthesized artificial life from inorganic atoms and molecules. Despite the awesome powers of twentieth-century science, which include the ability to manipulate life itself, science has not been able to synthesize even the most elemental artificial life-form. The biogenesis principle that only living things can give rise to other living things still holds firm: there is no experimental evidence that a living cell emerged from physical evolution. The genesis question reduces to whether, in theory, atoms and molecules could break the biogenesis principle and evolve into a living cell.

In effect, when it confronts biogenesis Darwinist reductionism argues against an established principle of science without benefit of evidence. Science presumes that its laws and principles hold true until it can be shown otherwise. We take these laws and principles as given and make our hypotheses from there. This is the default condition. It is unusual, to say the least, to assume that a principle, which has been verified countless times, can be contradicted without any evidence to support the assumption. Yet it seems to me that when it comes to explaining the origin of *life*, as opposed to mere species, this is precisely the situation in which Darwinist philosophy has finally put itself. It has assumed that the biogenesis principle can be broken and it ought to be called upon to show compelling evidence, the how and why.

Daniel Dennett, one of the more prominent current Darwinist partisans, for instance, has put it this way:

In describing the power of the central claim of Darwinism in the previous section, I helped myself to a slight (!) exaggeration: I said that every living thing is the descendant of a living thing. This cannot be true, for it implies an infinity of living things, a set with no first member.[1]

Explanations of this sort, however, do not really tell us why "an infinity of living things" cannot be true. Monotheistic thought has traditionally advocated an infinite living Being in the form of a Creator. Dennett repudiates this position and advocates "initially mindless and pointless algorithmic processes that gradually acquire meaning and intelligence as they develop."[2] But he just declares the traditional monotheistic position invalid, without actually demonstrating his case.

More particularly, how compelling is the scientific *evidence* for Dennett's kind of claims about a spontaneous origin of life that overrides the most obvious implication of the biogenesis principle? As it happens, he just gives us a brief 'chemical-free' overview of the so-called Cairns-Smith model, which argues that the precursors to life were silicate clays. And then he puts a highly revealing qualification in his footnotes,

> ... adding the warning that there are problems with Cairns-Smith's hypotheses, and balancing the warning with the reassurance that even if his hypotheses are all ultimately rejected – an open question – there are other, less readily understandable, alternatives to take seriously next.[3]

Here we ought to be asking: exactly what *scientific* reassurance can Dennett provide? In effect he is simply saying that, in his view, *there had to be* a non-living origin to life, and if the present model of this view fails he will just look for another one. This reduces to a mere belief or creed in its own right: it is *not* driven by the force of logical argument and the available scientific evidence. And, again, if Darwinism insists that the biogenesis principle can be broken in this way, then it ought to demonstrate compelling evidence as to how and why.

Fairness and equity, if you like, require that Darwinist thought have its feet held to the coals on this point, for it has rather deliberately set out to rob monotheistic philosophy of one of its most compelling arguments. The natural order of things is such that it takes a living thing to beget another living thing: the immediate implication is that a vital force exists somewhere, whether it is found within the universe or without. If the prestige of contemporary science, that Darwinist thinking wants to monopolize, cannot demonstrate the existence of such a vital force inside the universe, then it ought to acknowledge the possibility that this force lies elsewhere.

In this sense the principle of biogenesis levels the scientific playing field. Today, neither the Darwinian reductionist nor the monotheist offers a model that is entirely harmonious with contemporary scientific thinking. The former is violating an established principle of science without evidence, while the latter is arguing for a limit to natural explanation. To no small extent both positions are anathema to science, and science in its best sense should take a neutral stand, judging each model on its merits and the evidence. These at least are the ground rules for the argument in this chapter, as I understand them. On the one hand, I must show there is no compelling evidence life evolved from inanimate matter. On the other, I must show natural explanations are so inadequate to explain life's origins that there must be an intelligent Creator responsible for the whole affair.[4]

GENESIS IN BIOLOGY

Life from Outer Space

Origins always cause problems. Our wonderful universe had an origin. Logically it follows that life as we know it had an origin somewhere, and it is equally as perplexing to science as the origin of the universe. Planet Earth had an origin about 4.5 billion years ago and thus life on Earth had an origin as well. There is no eternal chain of living things stretching back into the mists of an infinite past: life came from somewhere. We have three options: life originated on the Earth; life originated in space; or life originated with a living God.

The notion that life came from outer space has a small following in the scientific community. Many scientists and a majority of the general public are convinced the universe is teeming with life, though at present we have no real evidence to support this conviction. Another sizeable number of people believe in so-called UFOs, even though the speed of light is held to be a fundamental constant which cannot be exceeded. This limits the amount of possible space travel to the nearest stars, at best. Possibly, theoretical physics will discover holes in the space-time continuum which may in theory at least allow intergalactic travel.

There is no logical objection to the proposition of life in outer space. Monotheists maintain God made the universe. If Earth is the only bio-planet, then God made an awfully large home for it. On the other side is the atheistic approach. Contingent self-ordering processes gave rise to an observer on Earth. If an observer arose on Earth, why not elsewhere? Yet the more we learn about the universe, the smaller is the number of possible solar systems that could be inhabited by intelligent beings like ourselves. The more or less obvious observations here refer to carbon-based life systems, the only form of life we know about. (I am not ruling out other forms, I just don't know if they exist and what they would look like.)

Evolution takes time so all the larger suns that burn out quickly are eliminated. All the slow-burning suns are eliminated because they do not provide sufficient energy. Only suns in the size range of our own would have the potential to support evolving life to intelligence. The majority of suns are twinned which makes it impossible to have stable planetary orbits. Unstable orbits decay, thus the planets involved in such orbits will fall into the sun; so that eliminates another large number straight out. Not all suns will have planets and not all those that do will have rocky planets like our own. Moreover, the rocky planets have to be larger than Mars and not much bigger than Earth and they have to have an orbit that keeps water in its liquid state – the average long-term temperatures must stay within zero and a hundred degrees Celsius. Finally, life must begin very early since the planet's heat-engine is quite finite in time.

Often overlooked is the presence of the three large planets further out. They play a vital role in protecting the Earth from meteor catastrophes, acting like giant gravitational vacuum cleaners for all kinds of solar debris. If there were only one giant planet, then Earth's orbit would be stretched out and conditions would become quite hostile for life. On the other hand, if the mass were distributed in a number of small planets the Earth would be hit repeatedly with catastrophic meteor collisions, constantly driving life backwards, if not to extinction. The result of all this nit-picking is that only a tiny fraction of the real estate of the universe could house life as we know it. A fraction of a great number is still a large number in its own right: even so, from a statistical point of view, life has to be a rare phenomenon in the universe. How rare or even unique it is has yet to be determined. Having said this, it is imperative not to loose sight of the primary argument. Essentially we want to know how life started, not how abundant it is. The interpretation of the significance of life's abundance or otherwise depends on its genesis, or how it started.

Francis Crick[5] and Fred Hoyle[6] are two members of the scientific community who have advocated the idea of an extraterrestrial origin of life. Both authors find common ground in the sheer difficulty of envisioning the process that gave rise to life on Earth. Hoyle, in particular, outlines some of the statistical horror stories one encounters in the spontaneous formation of life. He particularly elaborates on the difficulty of generating proteins which are the workhorses of life. If we leave everything to chance then generating a battery of useable proteins points to probabilities of one in a number followed by thousands of zeros. Any chance event involving numbers with hundreds of zeros, let alone thousands, is incomprehensible. Given the sobering magnitude of the statistical difficulties in generating life spontaneously, Crick and Hoyle have postulated some extraterrestrial origin of life.

Hoyle speculates that there are continuous showers of life raining down upon the Earth. The suggestion is they could travel along light waves creating a cosmic shower of bacterial life. He makes the telling point that some bacteria are unusually tolerant to radiation levels that could not be experienced at the Earth's surface. Likewise, some organisms are sensitive to ultraviolet light of very short wavelengths which they cannot have experienced for hundreds of millions of years. If this particular theory is correct then one would reasonably expect to find organic layers on the moon and on Mars. Both surfaces have been checked, however, and nothing of organic origin was found. Undoubtedly, it would have strengthened the theory immeasurably if the checking had uncovered some form of organic debris.

The surfaces of the moon and of Mars are quite inert: so if bacteria have been raining in from outer space then they would definitely have accumulated in these places. Some scientists argue the ultraviolet light would decompose any bacteria on the surface of Mars but one can't have it both ways. If bacteria can survive in outer space with no protection whatever, then they will have an enhanced chance of survival on Mars, where there is some atmospheric protection. Mars had water at one stage of its history. It is inconceivable that bacteria capable of surviving in outer space would find a water-rich Mars too hostile. This is especially true since the larger Earth was successfully colonized. Once established, these bacteria would have been capable of evolving with the Martian conditions. We have checked with the Viking explorer expeditions and there is no evidence of life on Mars.[7] Until these anomalies have been explained, the bacterial shower from outer space need concern us no further.

Crick, on the other hand, avoids the idea of random showers of bacteria from outer space. He advocates the seeding of the Earth by superior intelligences that are not God. He has suggested the bacteria could have been transported by some form of spaceship without being specific about the matter. But this idea appears to ignore some of the problems of travelling at the speed of light. Our present state of knowledge precludes us from travelling in excess of the speed of light. This in turn would confine all our future space explorations to a postage stamp relative to the enormity of the universe. In order to get the bacteria to us from any reasonable distance, it would appear necessary to call on enormous travel times. Theoretical physicists do talk of the possibility of holes in the fabric of space-time which might accommodate intergalactic travel. But these holes would also allow the intelligent Being to manipulate time itself. With the power to correct all errors of the past, one becomes involved with an infinite spiral of intelligence. The present puny human mind would be quite incapable of distinguishing these superior intelligences that were not God from that of God. The most telling argument against Crick is that his suggestion does not conform to the norms of scientific hypothesizing. To have a hypothesis in science, there must be some chance of its being either validated or repudiated. We know life has to have had an origin because the universe had an origin. The suggestion that superior intelligences seeded life on Earth 4 billion years ago only takes care of the origin of life on Earth. It tells us absolutely nothing about the origin of life itself, which is now lost in an unknown limbo of space and time. Such a suggestion can never be validated (or repudiated) and is thus beyond science.

A more particular problem that Crick appears not to have considered is the evolutionary time-scale. Many cosmologists would estimate the evolutionary time from the big bang to human intelligence in the region of 15 billion years. After the big bang it took a few billion years for the first galaxies and suns to form. Then supernovas had to explode with their heavy element constituents. The heavy elements had to be gathered up in a new solar system like our own. A good estimate for all of these events is 10 billion years and we have to add on another 5 or so billion years to evolve intelligence. In order to get a super intelligent life-form 4 billion years ago, we would need an age for the universe in the region of 20 billion years. We must also factor in travel time. It is more than probable Crick's hypothesis requires more time than the age of the universe, since most cosmologists put an upper limit to the age of the universe in the range of 18 to 20 billion years.

Implicit in Crick's suggestion are features we can deal with. The first is that there exist compelling reasons to believe there was a spontaneous origin of life somewhere: why make the suggestion otherwise? The second is that there should be reason to think there was advanced life-forms in the universe 4 billion years ago. However, there is no evidence anywhere, and there probably never can be, that life existed in space over 4 billion years ago. Such a conclusion could only be arrived at if life is shown to be a logical extension of atoms and molecules in the first place. This effectively returns us to the universe we know about and in particular the Earth. The third point here is that because life has not been seeded on Mars, Crick concedes that the target planets were stringently chosen. A lot of precautions were taken to avoid contaminating the Martian environment when the Viking 1 and 2 probes were sent up. There thus seems to be a fair degree of unanimity that bacteria could survive on the planet. We can conclude that Crick's 'space ship' must have had very specific instructions as to what were acceptable environmental parameters for the seeding of life.

Since Earth was chosen, it would seem that it had all the prerequisites for sustaining life from the beginning. This implies that Earth has all the prerequisites for spontaneously generating life in the first place. The alternative is that life's formation is favoured in one environment and its development in another. A defense of such a division between place of origin and development is impossible. Since life must have arisen spontaneously in an environment similar to Earth's, the problems involved can be adequately analyzed through reference to the physical and chemical conditions of Earth. In short, we can proceed as if life had arisen spontaneously on Earth.

This in fairness is the majority view among partisans of Darwinist thought today. The view that life originates with God, or even had some other extra-universal origin, can only be defended if it is shown that a spontaneous origin of life is, in effect, impossible. Hence, all three possible views of where life originated – the spontaneous-terrestrial, the spontaneous-extraterrestrial, and the extra-universal – ultimately depend on the question of whether or not life could have arisen spontaneously on Earth.

Setting the Stage on Planet Earth

Darwinian philosophy, and indeed the reductionism of contemporary science in general, is supposed to be grounded in the real world. All natural phenomena contain within them their own explanation. Science can and will explain everything. To be coherent, everything must be compellingly logical. Reductionists believe in the supreme rationality of science, such that everything in the entire universe can and will be explained by means of fundamental principles and processes. Everything logically reduces backwards and can be explained. The intelligent human being reduces to an ape; the ape reduces to a mammal; the mammal reduces to a reptile; and the reptile reduces to a fish, which reduces to a vertebrate, which reduces to a chordate, which reduces to a multicellular soft-bodied creature, which reduces to a nuclear-celled organism, which reduces to bacteria, which reduces to atoms and molecules, which reduce to whatever the final stuff of the real world turns out to be.

Measurement is the stuff of science. In science, the units of the properties that we measure, such as length, time, energy, mass, etc., are precisely defined. However, we have not been able to define a primary unit to measure complexity. At its most elemental level, we can relate the concept of complexity to behaviour: a lot of simple things are assembled to form an intricate 'whole' that exhibits complex behaviour. Complexity is a fundamental characteristic of the biological world, though it is also recognized in inferior form in the physical world. There is a marked discontinuity in organization and complexity between the most complex of physical systems and the most simple biological cell.

Any theory of genesis must bridge this gap. In simplest terms, a living cell is like a microscopic robot that is capable of duplicating itself. It is in every sense a molecular machine. Even in terms of our modern technology, this miniature robot is many orders of magnitude more complex and sophisticated than anything that humankind can fabricate. And this is the ultimate challenge presented to Darwinian reductionism: out of the raw 'stuff' of the primeval Earth it must show how the most complex machine known to man arose.

My own particular starting point here stresses that in its infancy, the Earth was a very violent, turbulent, and unstable place. This ancient period is referred to as the Hadean, after the classical name for hell. Rocks formed during this infernal period were consumed by the following convulsions of chaotic upheaval and thus left no trace at all. It is therefore unlikely, in the extreme, that an environment which failed to preserve rocks could have harboured the fragile molecules and cells of life. The oldest rocks known on Earth are around 4 billion years old. Since these are the first rocks to have survived the Hadean era, geological history begins at this point in time. Just as we use the word archaeology to characterize the study of, in some senses, very old (or ancient) human history, we use the word Archaean or ancient period for the beginning of geological history.

The Archaean, in this sense, was a violent and tumultuous place in its own right. The rocks of the Archaean indicate a state of continuous volcanic activity. Volcanic activity is known to be associated with the release of acids, sulphur, and metals: the so-called 'black smokers' on the bottom of the sea at present are depositing copper where they sit. In the Archaean there were probably very few of the granitic-type rocks that so characterize the present continental land mass. This means there were no continents 'floating' at the surface of the Earth as there are today. All the rocks at the surface of the Earth would have been dark green to black basic rocks, similar to basalt. Large mountains probably could not have existed, due to the inability of the hot plastic rocks underneath to support the weight of dense basaltic rocks. It is very likely that mega earthquakes were a regular feature of this environment, producing great tidal waves. We have no way of knowing how much water was present at the start, since both ice-rich meteorites and degassing from volcanoes could have added very considerably to the Earth's store of water. We can be pretty confident that the water which did exist was in constant violent agitation, with no land masses or plant life to moderate extreme disturbances.

There was no atmospheric oxygen in the Archaean so there was no protective ozone layer. Without this protective screen, a stream of high-energy light such as ultraviolet (UV) radiation poured continuously from the sun into the Earth's atmosphere and waters. High-energy radiation has the ability to break up large chemical molecules. When radiation does break up a molecule, it usually produces two molecules known as free radicals that are so chemically reactive that they react with a multitude of otherwise stable molecules. Most of us are familiar with the UV index from news reports. High-energy UV light has the ability to inflict severe sunburn and much worse, and to do permanent damage to the cell, leading to skin cancer. The hole in the ozone over Antarctica is responsible for the disturbing rise in skin cancer in Australia. If the entire ozone cover was lost all living things, with the exception of the blue-green algae and some other bacteria, would perish.

We can thus derive five plain-enough and rather significant conclusions about the early Archaean period: (1) the waters of the Archaean were very agitated, hence leading to high levels of mixing; (2) the waters of the Archaean were highly contaminated with a wide spectrum of chemical species; (3) the high-energy radiation made the early Archaean a very hostile environment for life as we know it; (4) any large molecules that existed in Archaean seas had a high probability of being broken apart by this radiation; and (5) the free radicals produced by the breakage of large molecules were highly reactive and were, in turn, able to react with virtually any other molecule they came in contact with.

Whatever the size of the oceans of this primeval Earth, they had to consist of one large reactive soup that was continuously being stirred and mixed. From the extreme volcanic activity, one would expect the waters were quite acidic and sulphurous in nature. They would have been saturated with sulphur, chlorine, bromine, and metals, such as iron, nickel, copper, zinc, lead, arsenic silver, and a host of others – as testified by the extensive metal deposits in Archaean rocks today. Because of the free radicals, all chemical species would have been in a continuous state of reaction. And the genesis of life must take place in this tumultuous cradle.

The Inorganic-Origin-of-Life Hypothesis

Most current accounts of the inorganic origin of life within this tumultuous Archaean cradle begin with Stanley Miller's experiments at the University of

Chicago.[8] Miller demonstrated that a mixture of water vapour, methane, ammonia, and hydrogen, under the influence of electrical discharges, could produce many organic molecules. In particular, he produced two amino acids, alanine and glycine. Since then, depending on the assumed initial conditions of the experiment, a whole suite of essential organic materials have been formed in a similar fashion. This, it is believed, lends tremendous credence to the so-called 'prebiotic soup' hypothesis on the spontaneous origin of life.

On this view the water bodies of the Earth, which were probably one continuous body at the time, were saturated with a vast number of carbon compounds. These carbon molecules were generated spontaneously by processes similar to Miller's. Some would claim that the ocean was like a broth of carbon compounds of about the same texture as chicken broth. With all this organic material floating around, it is believed to be an inexorable line of logic that all sorts of chemical reactions would lead progressively to more complex products. Finally, all the required molecules for life were built-up. Then the right combination of components coalesced and life began as a simple bacterium.

The Components of the Molecular Machine

My own view is that the spontaneous origin of life in the turbulent Archaean raises problems of a considerably greater magnitude than all this implies. To start with, when we speak of the evolution of the simplest of living cells we are discussing the emergence in nature of a microscopic automaton. In the final reduction of science, life is a molecular machine. Reducing the machine any further does not give us life but merely the components.

What sets the cell apart is an independent, self-regulating, and self-duplicating capacity. To achieve autonomous independence one has to have three fully integrated systems in operation simultaneously:

(1) There must be an information system, incorporating all the design and functions of the larger integrated system, and this information system must be capable of duplicating all and any of its information.

(2) There must be a communication system that can convey specific information correctly to each of the areas of operation, and feed information back from the operations areas to the information system.

(3) Finally, there must be an operation system that can utilize the information to operate, construct, supply, and repair all the components of the system, as well as provide the energy requirements of the whole cell.

The Proteins and the Complexity Restraint

In the molecular machine, the union of function, design, and operation between the proteins and DNA makes up the central core of the operation.

The proteins are the workhorses of the cell. To build such a system, we need specific proteins. The proteins have to be organized into energy transformers and a multitude of other enzymes. Enzymes can be thought of as proteins that have been equipped with an active chemical reaction site which has a particular shape, like a hole for a three-dimensional jigsaw piece. This allows a chemical reaction to go in a particular step. In energy extraction, the enzymes allow the controlled extraction of energy, bit by bit, rather than in one big burst like we see in fire. Virtually every enzyme is specific: it will do one job extraordinarily well and efficiently, but it is almost useless in doing anything else. Thus, all enzymes have to coordinated into 'teams' within the cell to perform each specific task. We can picture the cell as having batteries of enzymes lined up in different locations within its body performing their specific tasks.

All proteins in the cell are manufactured in organelles known as ribosomes. This manufacturing centre will be run by other proteins. We need to reproduce the exact proteins since inexact proteins are useless in the life process. We also need to have a repair centre – arguably one of the most spectacular properties of all living things. There are three overall steps in repair: a situation requiring repair has to be detected as a problem or irregularity; a solution to the problem must be devised and forthcoming; and then the solution must be executed. Repair is hardly a trivial property for anything. Proteins have to do all the work. They are the stuff of life, but they need to know what to do.

Next we need a regulatory centre, where all the blueprints for all the components are housed. We need a means of duplicating all the components and, even more spectacularly, we need a means of duplicating the duplication centre, so that the cell can multiply itself. This is the role of the genes in the cell. The genes and the proteins are in constant communication with each other through feedback mechanisms. The whole system must produce a cell flexible enough both to be tolerant to its environment and to incorporate the ability to evolve. The design has to be stable enough to survive at least 3.5 billion years of wear and tear.

Even for a moment, if we were to allow that all the specific chemicals could be spontaneously generated, how does one propose to allocate these enzymes by random means? It is like dismantling a working machine and by random means being able to reassemble it. Obviously, one's chances of success are inversely proportional to the complexity of the machine. The molecular machine is the most complex machine in the world, and the chances of assembling it by pure chance must be infinitesimal. Biologists have been stirring proteins and nucleotides, the building blocks of the genetic material, for over 40 years and they have never reported life. How many times during the Archaean period could such a perfect ensemble of life-components have come together? The biochemist in his laboratory has the ability to generate conditions almost infinitely more favourable than the Archaean conditions, and yet still no life has emerged.

The sheer complexity of the molecular machine also eliminates any serious consideration of a trial-and-error approach. In the Archaean waters where life must have begun, the haphazard appearance of a test tube full of all the correct types of amino acids and proteins, nucleotides, and membranes would have been a statistical fluke of the highest order. Even so, no scientist today armed with a multitude of test tubes containing all the correct ingredients has actually been able to synthesize life. The sobering reality is that the life components in a test tube are stubbornly uncooperative when it comes to creating the properties of self-organization.

Starting out with all the correct components of proteins and nucleotides no researcher has ever reported any significant self-organization amongst the components. What this means in reality is that even if we had an Archaean ocean rich with proteins and nucleotides, we have no evidence whatsoever that they could ever assemble themselves into a living cell. To have any credibility one needs to demonstrate that there were continuous supplies of proteins and nucleotides, and enormous stretches of time so as to allow some unknown self-ordering phenomenon to spontaneously arise. Yet none of this was actually available.

The Membrane Constraint

The problems just continue to mount from here. The proteins have to provide for a cell membrane, made up principally of a double layer of fatty molecules with some regulatory proteins embedded in it. The proteins in effect have to generate and maintain a giant two-molecule-wide fat molecule completely unlike themselves chemically. The secret of the membrane is that the fat molecule has a hydrophyllic or water-loving end and a hydrophobic or water-repelling end. The two-molecule layer of fat molecules is arranged so that the water-hating ends of the molecules are sandwiched in the middle of the two layers. This, in effect, creates an impermeable seal so as to set the system apart from the rest of the environment. At the same time a two-molecule-thick membrane can be made semi-permeable, allowing energy and materials to pass into the cell, while waste passes out.

The formation of the cell boundary represents a tremendous evolutionary event. For with it we now have two discrete systems demarcated by this boundary. On one side of this boundary we have the natural environment, and on the other we have the extreme order of life. How the first cell is supposed to have developed this adaptation is virtually inexplicable. What precise series of events will lead an inanimate chemical system to repair, maintain, and code for its own boundary is difficult to imagine.

No difficulty exists in forming oil droplets that could conceivably be turned into a membrane. But these droplets are inanimate. The difficulty is in showing how whatever goes on inside the droplets will 'learn' that there is a boundary, maintain this boundary, and code for the boundary. The independence of the cell's membrane leads to its independence from the immediate surroundings. This is the precondition for achieving homoeostasis – the fundamental characteristic of living cells, whereby the cell acts as one collective whole in its ability to maintain a steady chemical balance in a changeable environment. Homoeostasis requires a series of chemical controls and complex feedback cycles which ensure that every chemical species in the cell is produced and maintained in correct proportions.

The more complex a system becomes, the more vulnerable it becomes to destabilizing fluctuations that reduce it to chaos. It follows that the more complex a system becomes, the more and more restricted becomes its configuration. At the highest levels of complexity there usually exists only one 'privileged' configuration. Any deviation from the privileged configuration reduces the system to immediate chaos. Considering the cell's complexity, the importance of the membrane in this respect is clear enough.

The presence of the membrane would also appear to determine where all the significant evolutionary events took place in the spontaneous origin of life. They must have occurred inside the membrane, otherwise there would be no purpose in developing the membrane in the first place. The development of the membrane would have to be considered a most fortuitous occurrence, since it is now indispensable for individual cells. Restricting all the significant evolutionary events to within prebiotic membranes drastically reduces the opportunity for anything interesting to happen. It constitutes a major restraint on the spontaneous-origin-of-life hypothesis. The probability is constrained by the number and availability of pre-life membranes that existed.

Since the Archaean is the geological period of reference, one must ask how long an oil droplet could hope to survive in such turbulent and violent conditions? We know from oil spillages that turbulent waters are effective agents in breaking up and dispersing oil. Add in free radicals and UV light and it would appear to be extremely difficult to maintain the integrity of oil droplets for any period of time. The membrane problem is also a major obstacle to any altogether convincing theory on the spontaneous origin of life, since we have no hypothesis to explain how the cell discovered it had a membrane in the first place. Indeed, separating the homeostatic complexity of a living cell from its membrane appears to be contradictory: the two need to occur simultaneously. In this light, how genetic nucleotides code for proteins that organize a giant fat molecule is quite mysterious.

The Chemical Probability Constraints

At this point the plot begins to thicken in some very dramatic ways. Before some unknown self-ordering phenomenon could assemble suites of proteins and nucleotides inside a membrane into a living cell, the proteins and nucleotides must first be generated. In truth it is most difficult to manufacture suitable proteins and nucleotides. Starting with the primitive Earth we can envision a biotic soup all over the oceans. The inorganic molecules are formed by various elementary molecules in the Earth's atmosphere and the energy is provided by sunlight,[9] volcanicity, lightning discharges, and heat from radioactive decay.

As far as I am concerned, the chemist is free to start with any environment he so chooses: for if he can generate life from any completely inorganic environment of his choosing, then the case is closed – the spontaneous origin of life has some probability no matter how small. So far there has been no success in this endeavour. This is not as generous an offer as it may sound. In 1969 it took six weeks of the most advanced chemistry to synthesize the enzyme ribonuclease. One can only speculate endlessly on how long it would take to synthesize the same enzyme by trial and error.

Experimental evidence is very significant. It is abundantly clear that a knowledgeable biochemist in a well-equipped laboratory is fully capable of generating products that have only remote possibilities of being generated by chance in the natural environment. Just starting with all the right chemicals in the right place represents a statistically unique event. The next favouring element is the intelligence, knowledge, and expertise of the biochemist, and his knowledge of what it is he is trying to do. This latter point has often been overlooked. The biochemist is not being asked to produce a new invention: he is simply being asked to copy the design of an existing entity. He knows what it looks like, and he knows its properties, characteristics, and composition. We can never quantify this factor, but it is fair to say there are few if any inorganic compounds on the surface of the Earth that chemists cannot synthesize. Whatever else, the lab evidence undermines the notion that life can be viewed as the inevitable and logical end-product of random chemical reactions, taking place under the influence of a continuous supply of energy.

In science, lab evidence carries more weight than theory. If a chemist can synthesize a bacterium from inanimate chemicals, then there is no longer an argument: a random process could conceivably follow the same path, given enough time. The failure to do so must likewise carry weight. Human intelligence has produced marvels in all sorts of areas of technology. Yet it has quite dramatically failed to produce life. This point is amply reinforced by the fact that we are now using living organisms and genetic engineering to synthesize proteins rather than synthesizing them from scratch. We have not even considered the notion of generating new artificial proteins, since we cannot even figure out how to design one. Some success has been reported with ribonucleic acid or RNA molecules, but to offer any hope at all the proteins have to help catalyze the nucleotides and the nucleotides have to catalyze the proteins. Some researchers have used specific protein catalysts from living cells to synthesize nucleic acids but this, in a sense, is cheating. After 40 years of intensive research, there is no report of any self-ordering worth talking about. Not one protein has ever been reported as the product of far-from-equilibrium self-ordering events.[10] The void in our knowledge refuses to be filled by any form of elementary principle or process.

In the prebiotic soup postulate let us concede for the sake of argument that there were many inorganic carbon molecules present. To build a protein we need a supply of the 20 basic building blocks known as amino acids. Perhaps it is possible all 20 amino acids were present in the Archaean period, but how does one concentrate them? In essence, how do they find each other so as to be able to react in the first place? The total concentration of amino acids would have been only a tiny fraction of all the molecules present. The amino acids used by life to make proteins are pure compounds of carbon, hydrogen, nitrogen, oxygen, and some sulphur. How can pure compounds be synthesized out of the chemical chaos of the Archaean?

There is no known way of selecting only amino acids for reaction purposes outside of the living cell. This leads one to the conclusion that whatever process gave rise to life in the Archaean must have had a means of producing the amino acids rather than selecting them ready-made from the environment. We have run headlong into the void: there is no natural process outside of life which can generate amino acids exclusively. There is no simple explanation as to how a purification process could have been set in motion spontaneously. Purifying chemical reactants so as to have a reaction proceed in a desired direction is the hallmark of our modern technology. It is based on knowledge and intelligence, and this once again implies that whatever steps take place in the origin of life require intelligence as well.

The amino acids used by life in the synthesis of proteins are surprisingly specific. Your left and right hands are identical except for their orientation in space: they are mirror images of each other. Just as your hands are left and right versions of an otherwise identical form, so too are 19 of the 20 fundamental amino acids that go to produce the proteins. The problem this poses is that the left- and right-handed molecules have identical chemical and physical properties, except that they rotate polarized light differently. When synthesized artificially, an equal number of left- and right-handed amino acids form. It is the life process that sets them apart (which of course is putting the cart before the horse, because we have to start in the Archaean when no life was present). Thus, under Archaean conditions we are obliged to assume equal numbers of left- and right-handed amino acids. And somehow we have to obtain only left-handed amino acids, because protein structure is all important to life.

Proteins are the workhorses of the living cell and enzymes are the prima donnas of proteins. It is the remarkably precise structure of an enzyme which allows it to perform as many as a thousand actions a second: thus, whatever generates enzyme structure is critical to life. This, in turn, is due to the fact enzymes are composed exclusively of left-handed molecules. Thus the prerequisite for life is to be able to have an exclusive source of these left-handed molecules, so as to facilitate enzyme reactions. What I am suggesting is that there is no possibility of having a lesser-organized version of life. It is obligatory to build the proteins out of left-handed molecules because only left-handed molecules are used in the life process at present. Once again we hit the void. Outside of life, science knows of no natural process which can select left- or right-handed amino acids. Until one can demonstrate a natural process, with the property of selecting or producing only left-handed amino acids, the spontaneous-origin-of-life hypothesis must be judged as rather fatally flawed.

The opposite (but otherwise identical) problem is found in the nucleic acids that make up the genes. Nucleic acids are macro-molecules made up of individual building blocks called nucleotides. The sugar in the nucleotide is either ribose or deoxyribose and they are both right-handed. Thus the individual nucleotides are all right-handed and they combine to form the famous right-handed double helix of DNA. The well-studied bacterium E. coli is believed to have been around for well over a billion years and it is representative of one of the most simple organisms available. It has about 4.2 million units in its genetic molecule DNA. If the initial bacterium had a tenth of this DNA to start with, we would need 400,000 right-handed nucleotides to produce a perfect right-handed double helix.

The key word here is 'perfect.' A duplication process which is not perfect is in effect useless. The ultimate trick of heredity is that the genes can copy themselves. To facilitate this copying property the right-handed double helix has to be structurally perfect. Nothing less will suffice due to the avalanche of errors that would result. There would seem to be no seriously conceivable chance that a 400,000-unit right-handed double helix could be arrived at by trial and error. Once again, what is required is a process that can systematically generate only left- or right-handed molecules. Life is obviously one process: a skilled chemist can do the same with considerable difficulty; but we know of no other means of achieving this objective. Then we have to demonstrate a whole range of intermediate and stable molecules that would allow us to gradually approach the 400,000-unit molecule. But chemists have still not succeeded in doing this either.

For whatever reason, science has made virtually no progress in demonstrating how such a stringently selective process could have taken place in the contaminated waters of the Archaean environment. In 40 years of laboratory effort, nobody has succeeded in synthesizing nucleotides from their component elements. No matter what trick the biochemist turns to, the nucleotides tend to dissociate faster than they can be synthesized. It appears as if it would have been next to impossible for any nucleotide to have persisted in the Archaean waters, let alone a 400,000-unit right-handed double helix. Building the genetic material by natural spontaneous processes has defied the greatest efforts of modern science. The only progress has been made through cheating, when biochemists use suitable catalysts which were originally produced by other living cells. The great void in our knowledge about the ordering phenomenon responsible for the genesis of life refuses to yield to elementary principles and processes of science.

No law of organic chemistry exists suggesting that the amino acid bond found in proteins is the only way of reacting amino acids with each other. In fact, when water is present normal laws of chemistry predict that proteins will decompose rather than form. This happens because water is expelled or dehydrated for each pair of amino acids we combine in a protein bond, and when the reaction occurs in water, dehydration of this sort is not favoured. If we are trying to react 100+ amino acids together, energy must be supplied to the reaction and the specific protein bond site must be protected. Otherwise all sorts of other reactions will occur. A skilled chemist can do this with great difficulty: to do it spontaneously is beyond comprehension. Perhaps a protein could be formed spontaneously, but simultaneously many junk molecules will also form. The only known natural process reacting the amino acids in the right way is the life process, but this just adds to the uniqueness of life. The extremely specific chemistry of the life process is not found anywhere else.

Given that we are going to react amino acids together, we should note that a staggering number of permutations exists in the way they can be put together. If we try to assemble a 250-molecule-long chain with 20 different amino acids, an immense number of possible permutations present themselves. Of these, only a small fraction have been used over the entire history of life. Some figures that have been suggested are: the number of possible combinations is a number with around 320 zeros in it; the estimated number of useful proteins ever used in the life process is a number with around 52 zeros in it; and the rough ratio of useful proteins to useless proteins compares to a number with 270 zeros. What these numbers tell us is this: if undirected processes generate proteins, then those proteins used in the life process will be forever lost in a sea of other proteins. This problem compounds when we try to get the 'useful' proteins together.

It has been argued that the simplest possible organism would need a few thousand chemical species to achieve homoeostasis. This in turn implies we would need many hundreds of proteins. Even under these specifications the organism would be classified as a simple organism which in reality does not exist. We have been having difficulties in generating one protein, let alone hundreds. To calculate the probability of generating a hundred proteins, just calculate the probability of one and multiply this probability by itself a hundred times. When you do the calculations all you end up with is an incomprehensible improbability.

As an example, the enzyme cytochrome c, which was mentioned in relation to the biological classification system in the last chapter, is fundamental to energy conversions in all cells. The probability that this enzyme could come about by random processes is one in a number with 130 zeros. Generating a hundred enzymes of cytochrome c would leave us with a probability that has some 13,000 zeros. And even astrophysics doesn't generate numbers of this magnitude. The truth of the matter, however, is that these huge numbers actually exaggerate the possibility of the event. To be of any use at all, the required proteins must come together in the same place and time. If this does not happen, they will be lost in a sea of 'useless' proteins and other undesirable chemical species. Without some form of guiding force I, myself, cannot see how this could possibly happen.

All these problems with proteins just get us to the beginning of the real problem; generating the extraordinary levels of organization and complexity typical of life. If chance processes were to generate hundreds or even thousands of proteins, there is a near-infinite probability against the ability of these proteins to synchronize together and perform useful tasks. Once again, biochemists can put all the right chemicals together but they don't produce life. All the preceding arguments have been suggesting that just getting the right chemicals together and synthesizing proteins from them is a practical impossibility in the Archaean environment. Yet this only represents the beginning of the problem and not the end. This realization was a turning-point in my own thinking on the origin of life. From the perspective of the Earth sciences, the rules of the debate on the spontaneous origin of life have been fixed.

The Archaean period of geological history is our reference point here. I readily concede the possibility that all the fundamental building blocks of life were generated spontaneously during this period. In return, I would expect reductionist partisans to concede that virtually every other possible chemical species was also generated spontaneously. In essence, with respect to the Archaean, the required concentration of life's building blocks cannot be demonstrated. However, virtually nobody factors in the conditions of the Archaean, and in this respect it seems to me what we get amounts to sanitized science. Let me just outline some of my concerns about phosphorous as an example.

Phosphorous is a minor element in the crust of the Earth, which means its concentration is between 0.1 and 1.0 percent. It is geochemically associated with iron, and with living things as well (but that occurs later). It is essential in the functioning of cell membranes, cellular energy transformations, and the construction of the nucleic acids in the genes – among other functions. In fact, the important role of phosphorous is one of the arguments for only one original cell at the beginning of all life. For life as we know it, phosphorous is important.

Archaean rocks are not rich in phosphorous, and the only way to provide the phosphorous necessary for life in this environment was through erosion of phosphorous-rich minerals found in igneous rocks. This, to my mind, settles any discussion as to whether water was present in the early Archaean: life could not emerge without phosphorous, and so water had to be present to leach it from the rocks. But protein and nucleotide synthesis are both dehydration reactions, which means they are not favoured in the presence of water. Energy has to be supplied to make the reaction go. But phosphorous happily forms minerals with metals and other elements that must have been quite abundant in the Archaean environment.[11] How can we account for phosphorous associating in carbon molecules and not appearing in any notable concentration in mineral form? I don't know the answer and I doubt if anybody else does either. Darwinian and other reductionist partisans have simply decided to ignore the problem, along with a host of other similar conundrums.

Having thus fixed the rules of the game, all science has achieved is to arrive at the starting point and not the end. This gets back to the great void in our knowledge. We clearly need a process to explain the ordering of the affairs of life, but we simply do not have one. Yet there is no escaping this need. Something had to direct the synthesis of the proteins and nucleotides – chance cannot do the job. The greatest statistical impossibility of them all is the coordination of the genes and the proteins as in the ribosome.

In the very end, the essence of reductionist explanation is that life and all its processes can be reduced back to its chemistry, and then fully explained by the elementary principles and processes of science. On the surface, this is an intellectually attractive proposition, but neither reductionist partisans nor anyone else can demonstrate any process whereby raw chemical constituents can be synthesized into proteins and nucleotides. The proposition would be in even more difficulty, if that is possible, were it to factor in the contamination of the Archaean waters in which life must have begun. It is impossible to complete a process without first beginning it. Until the day comes when biochemists can demonstrate a natural process which generates proteins made out of left-handed amino acids, and a long right-handed macro molecule of DNA, there is no strict scientific *evidence* for the spontaneous origin of life.

UNDERLYING CONTRADICTIONS IN THE PHILOSOPHY OF REDUCTIONISM

The Spontaneous-Origin-of-Life Hypothesis from Another Angle

There is another set of crucial weaknesses in what the philosophy of reductionism implies about 'the genesis of life,' and I think it deserves some sustained attention. To start with, the logic of modern biology reduces to the logic of the information in the genes. Evolution, the greatest ordering process ever discovered by humankind, is at heart a genetic process. The core of the genesis problem is we have no genes to do the ordering. If genes are responsible for running life and genes are responsible for the magnificence of biological evolution, what is responsible for the genes?

In this setting, the spontaneous-origin-of-life hypothesis cries out for some unknown evolutive force. The monument that biological evolution has carved out for itself came at the direction of the genes. Now we must search for whatever generated the genes in the first place. Which is greater: that which generated the order of the biological world, or that which generated that which generated the order of the biological world? The ultimate responsibility for biological order is the process that generated the gene-directed living cell. That it could be otherwise is logically inconceivable. One must account not only for the first living cell but also for the extraordinary potential for evolution that came with it. Thus, in terms of complexity, the origin of life stands as the supreme ordering event humanity has ever become aware of. And this presents an immense problem in philosophy. We have already argued that biological evolution is the most complex ordering phenomenon known to humankind. But now we are obliged to deduce that there exists an even more profound ordering phenomenon, that is not genetically directed and about which modern science knows nothing at all!

The immensity of this void in our scientific knowledge cannot be overstated. Since science deals exclusively with natural causes, the unknown ordering process leading to the emergence of life must logically derive from the world of physical evolution. Once it assembled the magnificent gene-directed living cell, with its enormous inherent evolutionary potential, this unknown process of nature just disappeared! It vanished right out of the universe and left all subsequent evolution up to the genes. Any ordering process which fabricates a living cell surely can do other wondrous tricks. Yet there is no evidence that any other trick was performed. The truth is that there is no evidence of anything other than the origin of a unique gene-directed living cell. This is damning in its own right. If natural phenomena hold within themselves their own explanation, then a process so powerful as the evolutionary transition from inanimate matter to animate matter must manifest itself in other ways. This simply has not happened and no obvious explanation exists to explain the exclusivity of the process.

We can trace the history of the universe back to a fraction of a second after the big bang without calling for new types of laws – such is our knowledge of the physical world and physical evolution. Yet in the origin of life, some new law or force hitherto unknown must be invoked. When reductionist partisans resort to conjuring up statistical magic in their attempts to explain the genesis of life, they are in effect giving us a measure of the immensity of our ignorance. The whole reductionist case is self-contradictory. In reductionist thinking, a natural phenomenon should contain its own explanation. How can the unique event of the origin of life contain its own logical explanation? If the origin is not unique, where are the other events and why has science not discovered the physical process responsible? Given the present state of our knowledge, the origin of life must be judged a most unnatural event.

Life and Death

Another peculiar aspect of reductionist philosophy turns around its conviction that life must reduce to inanimate physical processes in the first place. This flies in the face of current scientific evidence that only living things can give rise to other living things – the principle of biogenesis. Given the empirical strength of the principle, the absence in the mainstream scientific community of some default hypothesis that incorporates biogenesis is somewhat surprising. One might expect contemporary science to advocate the existence of a vital force (as the French philosopher Henri Bergson did in the earlier years of the twentieth century), or some other fundamental principle of life in the universe.[12]

A clearly related aspect of biology is the irreversibility of biological death. No living thing can cheat death. No biochemist can reanimate an organism once it is dead. The chemical constituents of a dead organism degrade and are reabsorbed by the local environment. The local environmental condition and biological death are one and the same. The spontaneous-origin-of-life hypothesis, however, suggests that life came out of the chemistry of the environment. And this implies that life came out of the state we know as death and, thus, that death itself must be spontaneously reversible. Yet of course science is incapable of reversing death. The reductionist hypothesis on the spontaneous origin of life contradicts two of the most fundamental characteristics of life as we know it.

In strict reductionist thinking the reason for death is hard to comprehend. If life is an inexorable line of logic from inanimate molecules, why does the process have to reverse itself for every living organism? Why should the individual ordered phase of life have to collapse, while the wider phenomenon of life continues uninterrupted? Given how reductionism proposes to explain the origin of life, these are most difficult questions. On the other hand, biological death is a prerequisite in the evolution of complex organisms. If the first organism which jumped from inanimation to life had not been prone to die, then there would have been very little turnover of individual organisms. This would have led to a biologically static world in which new individuals were produced only as and when there was room for them.

Just as the fundamental forces of the universe had to be carefully balanced so as to facilitate complex evolution, the symmetry between life and death also had to be balanced. If there is excessive death, then extinction results; if there is excessive longevity, then stagnation results. In evolution, time is the variable allowing complex entities to emerge. Biological time is greatly amplified by biological death, which in turn allows for great complexity, such as the human brain, to emerge in a finite duration. Thus without death, biological complexity would not have had enough time to emerge. In reductionist thinking, biological death is the failure of the individual. But biological evolution can only take place in terms of the individual. Thus it is the failure of the individual to evolve or maintain longevity which promotes the eventual success of biological evolution. Evolution on this view must work in the present: it cannot anticipate the needs of tomorrow. As I have pointed out in earlier chapters, evolution is a characteristic of life. Biological death is anticipating the need for biological evolution but it has absolutely no value to any individual. And this appears to contradict reductionism at its core.

Similar evolutionary purposefulness can be seen in the need for biogenesis. If we believe it is possible for different life-forms to spontaneously emerge from inorganic elements, then we must also expect different types of genetic systems. One of the reasons for the success of bacteria is their ability to exchange genetic information in what might be described as bacterial sex. If the format of their genetic codes was not compatible, then the bacteria could not conquer every physical environment: in fact, they would probably be quite restricted.

One of the great evolutionary leaps was to generate the nuclear cell. Nearly all authorities agree the nuclear cell came about through a long process of symbiosis between individual bacteria. In the end, the bacteria coalesced genetically to form the nuclear cell. Similarly, the chloroplasts in plant cells, which are responsible for photosynthesis in plants, are believed to be ancient blue-green algae, which have become incorporated into the larger cell. These fundamental evolutionary steps would have been impossible if the organisms were employing incompatible genetic systems. They all had to share a similar genetic format before they could permanently amalgamate into the larger cell. The simplest way to ensure compatible genetic systems is to restrict all genetic systems to one format.

The same format for the genetic code is found throughout biology. After 4 billion years of evolution and uncountable numbers of duplications, the formats of the genetic code of a bacterium and a human being are compatible. Without this consistency of format, little of interest in biological evolution could have emerged. Drawing parallels with the stringent balances between the fundamental forces of the universe is almost unavoidable. The organization of the universe is devised to evolve complex planets with complex elements, in orbits around long-lasting suns, over immense periods of time. Similarly, the organization of biology is set up to evolve complex organisms over long stretches of time. Biogenesis and the 'coincidence' of an invariant format for the genetic code ensure compatibility of the genes.

Given that evolution or change is a characteristic of living things over geological time, it is next to impossible to conceive how a fixed format for the genetic code could arise. Life's evolutionary potential and its genetic code appeared with the first living cell. The fixed format of the genetic code looks deliberate and purposeful: life appears to be designed to evolve.

The Feast/Famine Paradox

Reductionist partisans of the spontaneous-origin-of-life hypothesis also propose that a relatively simple bacterium arose in an environment having the consistency of an organic soup. They essentially argue that an ocean full of organic molecules will somehow lead to the development of proteins and nucleotides, which in due course will assemble themselves into a living cell.

Yet what happens after this is something of a paradox. The logical paradox of self-reference, for instance, is well-known to mathematicians. You are handed a sheet of paper. On one side there is a statement, "The proposition on the opposite side is true." On the other side is the statement, "The proposition on the other side is false." One cannot resolve the resulting conflict because of the inherent self-reference involved.

The same holds true for our first bacterium. Reductionism implies that the original environment was so benign that life just had to evolve. Yet once life began it must, as a consequence, have found itself in a benign environment. A bacterium will do what bacteria do so well: it will replicate. Now this bacterium, being the first living thing, has no enemies and literally has the world to itself. If it only doubled its population at a rate of close to once a day, which by bacterial standards is close to paralysis, then in 20 days there are over a million bacteria. In 40 days there will be a trillion, and in 80 days a trillion trillion – a number with 24 zeros. In 160 days the number will have 48 zeros, and in 320 days 96 zeros. The problem is obvious enough: in less than a year our bacterium will have a greater mass by at least 26 orders of magnitude than the entire visible universe. In less than three months, the prebiotic soup will be degraded and life will end.

It is inconceivable that the inorganic production of carbon compounds could in any way sustain a thriving population of bacteria. It is equally impossible to concentrate the inorganic food for these bacteria. Moreover, we can hardly hope to evolve our way out of the problem in such short periods of time. Thus the very logic leading to life leads to its destruction also. In the analogy of the paradox of self-reference, the environment takes the place of the paper. And then we can say the environment is so good that life must start, and simultaneously we can say the environment is so good that life must end.[13] And in the end there is no resolution to this paradox.

Even more problems present themselves with this initial bacterium. Darwinist thought has typically assumed that the first organism would have a simple metabolic chemistry, along the line of a fermenting organism today. What the reductionist partisans would really like is for the nineteenth-century idea of simple life to be true. In this way they could argue for a long series of gentle jumps in organic complexity rather than the Grand Canyon between inorganic molecules and the living cell. Nature has been cruelly uncooperative in this matter. The energy output from fermentation is only in the region of six percent of that produced by aerobic respiration in cells like our own.

How on Earth is such an inefficient system expected to support incomplete mutations with such precarious supplies of food?

An interesting aspect of bacteria has also come to light from genetic engineering. If one induces a bacterium to produce enzymes it does not need, then the extra effort involved so enfeebles the organism that it is scarcely capable of survival at all. In short, when we humans tamper with the genetics of bacteria, they universally become a weaker strain, with measurably reduced vitality.

Another feature of genetic engineering is that if we introduce extra genetic material, such as a plasmid, into a bacterium, then over a few generations the bacteria will tend to get rid of it. Bacteria have a tendency to act as if they were streamlined, and they get rid of any extra baggage rather quickly. Even the genes of a bacterium have the look of being streamlined for immediate action. They look as if they were designed to produce immediate responses to the environment. As I mentioned in the last chapter, the accumulation of non-lethal neutral errors in the genome is occurring at an incredibly slow pace. If bacteria did not have a correction mechanism for errors, they would drown in a sea of neutral errors over geological time. Thus, the accumulation of mutations in organisms like these bacteria is extremely difficult.

Reductionism has run into such confounding situations as a result of its insistence on the existence of simpler life-forms. Photosynthesis is the energy cornerstone of life. The vast majority of organisms that have ever lived have depended either directly or indirectly on photosynthesis. Thus photosynthesis is an integral component of the logic of life. But it is impossible to evolve a photosynthesizing organism directly from inanimate molecules. When reductionism tries to avoid the impossibility of generating a photosynthesizing organism directly from inanimate molecules, it contradicts the logic of life as we know it.

The Evolution of Complexity Requires Time

In the world of contingent evolution, time is king. Given enough time, even the most fantastically improbable succession of events becomes defensible. The trend in geology has been for successive pieces of evidence to push the origin of life progressively backwards in time. For a very long time, there was no evidence of life below the base of the Cambrian period, 575 million years ago. Indeed, nobody could even find a hint to the beginning of Earth's history: it was simply lost in the mists of time itself. This left unlimited amounts of time to conjure up life from inert chemicals. The evidence fit perfectly with the prevailing notions of simpler life-forms. It was eminently reasonable to propose that such simple life could arise spontaneously over stretches of time defying human imagination.

Today, however, simple life-forms are known not to exist, and one geological find after another has relentlessly driven back the allowable date of the origin of life. There is now unequivocal evidence in Western Australia of advanced photosynthesizing bacteria some 3.5 billion years ago. This bacterial life had a form almost identical to blue-green algae (or cyanobacteria). The bacteria lived in circular-like colonies known as stromatolites. There is a great quantity of fossil stromatolites in ancient rocks, but very few living forms. Some modern stromatolites have been found in Shark Bay, Australia, in very salty or brackish waters. They consist of colonies of blue-green algae that build up layers of sedimentary-like mats in their colony. These mats eventually accrete into hard circular rocks. And we are now able to identify the stromatolitic structure in ancient rocks from these living stromatolites.

For strict Darwinian reductionism, these results are nearly calamitous. Time is the one variable in the evolutionary equation which can generate complexity. With the loss of 3 billion years, reductionist thought is faced with a very compressed time frame. Given that conditions in the Hadean era were too extreme for life, reductionism must argue for the origin of life and the emergence of photosynthesis in a period not exceeding 500 million years. This is an immense duration but, alas, not long enough to argue that life must logically emerge.

The Present Is the Key to the Past

In a similar context it is worth noting that contemporary reductionist thought has largely broken with the philosophy underpinning Darwin's original thesis. Darwin was deeply influenced by the geological maxim that "the present is the key to the past." If we look at the present situation, photosynthesis is the cornerstone of life. Life without photosynthesis would reduce to small populations of organisms around volcanic vents – the so-called archaebacteria. In excess of 99.99 percent of all living organisms depend directly or indirectly on photosynthesis for survival. The entire logic to life on Earth rests on there being an organic means of harnessing the sun's energy. Nobody anywhere suggests that a photosynthesizing organism could have arisen spontaneously from inorganic molecules. Thus, to save its theory reductionism postulates simpler organisms as a transition phase.

This suggestion violates present conditions on two counts: it completely ignores the prevailing importance of photosynthesis; at the same time, one of the consistent findings of contemporary science is that there is no such thing as a simple bacterium. The complexity of the simplest of living cells is orders of magnitude greater than anything found in the physical universe. Non-phoosynthesizing simple bacteria are needed by reductionist theory and not by any demands of the scientific evidence. In fact, the evidence suggests that non-photosynthesizing bacteria probably could not exist in the first place, and would simply starve to death even if they could. In its efforts to 'make its theory fit,' reductionist thought has increasingly entangled both itself and contemporary science in a maze of contradictions.

The Second Law of Thermodynamics and Probability

The second law of thermodynamics states that, given a process proceeding in a finite time from A to B, the amount of unavailable energy known as entropy increases. This law stipulates that the only processes that may occur are those producing a net increase in the entropy of the system and its surroundings combined. No matter what process is considered, the entropy change is always positive. It represents a profound barrier to what is possible, since we may never construct a process that leads to a net decline in entropy. When stated like this, there is no disagreement among scientists about the second law. The controversy arises when we try to apply the second law.

Ludwig Boltzmann related the second law's increase in entropy to probability. Entropy grows because probability grows, and that means there is a consistent trend in nature to favour the more probable states. These states are characterized by an ever-increasing symmetry and a levelling out of differences. What Boltzmann's probability means is that physical things can never organize themselves on their own: organization requires outside input. The origin of life is the singular organizing event of all time. If life arose spontaneously, then atoms and molecules must have organized themselves in a radical violation of Boltzmann's formulation of the second law. No scientific hypothesis can violate the second law and survive. But life has evolved greater and greater levels of complexity, culminating with human intelligence. If life had outside information to start with, this evolutionary sequence of increasing complexity would not represent a violation of the second law. Some branches of contemporary Darwinist reductionism have countered with self-ordering systems.

The Self-Ordering System

It is abundantly clear that trial and error cannot be responsible for the origin of life. The compression of the time factor gives the *coup de grace* to any notion of there being room for a statistical fluke in the origin of life. What is needed is some means of directing the origin of life. The mechanics of Darwinism today are those of a self-ordering system. It is possible that a physical self-ordering system gave rise to life and thus the self-ordering system continues to drive life to ever higher levels of evolved complexity. Thus, at the very root of organic evolution there may lurk the mechanics of a physical self-ordering system. This would constitute the directing force needed for the origin of life and its subsequent evolution. In the final reduction the organic world, though enormously complex due to the self-ordering drive, is a physical process like any other.

Much of the pioneering work on understanding self-ordering phenomena has been done by Nobel laureate Ilya Prigogine.[14] Prigogine and others suggest that the world of complexity relates to the general behaviour of all systems and is not the sole preserve of biological systems. They further point out that under opportune conditions, some physical systems can give rise to self-ordering phenomena. In order for a self-ordering phenomenon to occur in a system, the system itself must be far from equilibrium, or out of balance, and there must be a continuous flow of energy or materials into the system. It can be argued these preconditions were met in the Archaean environment, with the sun pouring in energy in the form of light radiation (though it is not clear just how far from equilibrium the ancient Earth's system was).

A system may experience a self-ordering phenomenon if a certain critical moment is reached. At this stage a chance event occurs that is not repressed or dampened by the rest of the system. On the contrary, the exact opposite happens: the chance event is amplified or magnified, and it is this phenomenon which leads to self-organization within the system. In these systems a very small event or fluctuation can lead to very dramatic results, producing changes in the entire system that can be orders of magnitude greater than the initial fluctuation.

The laser is a machine which exploits this phenomenon. When you start up the laser, all sorts of light waves are produced in what is known as the transition. Then, by chance, the particular wavelength the machine is designed for is produced. The self-ordering phenomenon sets in at this stage. Rather than being dampened or lost, the desired wavelength induces other wavelengths to be similar to itself until all the wavelengths are the same. This in effect produces a very ordered beam of light out of a chaotic beam. Other well-known examples in the physical world are convection cells in liquids and chemical clocks.[15]

Biological systems are full of examples of chemical feedback that either enhance the system or depress it. In fact, biological systems are such wonderful examples of self-ordering phenomena that Prigogine is inclined to give a great many biological examples. Nobody denies the validity of what Prigogine says about biological systems: they are truly amazing in their ability to self-organize and self-regulate with positive feedback, negative feedback, cross feedback, and so forth. Yet in the context of the spontaneous origin of life, there are no biological systems available, and that means we must confine ourselves to inanimate systems. And in this context, Prigogine has failed to demonstrate anything on the order of biological complexity in the inanimate world. What is fundamentally missing from his work is an example of a continuously evolving system of chemicals that starts simple and passes through a series of clearly defined complex states, with each one more complex than the one before. The evolution of the light beam in the laser stops at the desired wavelength: it does not evolve on to further levels of complexity.

Interference is the Achilles heel of self-ordering phenomena. Remove the mirror from the laser and the desired wavelength cannot reach its critical point, and hence no amplification occurs. Currents destroy the convection system in Benard cells, and chemical clocks disintegrate in the presence of other chemicals. Interfere with the integrity of the cell's membrane and the chaos of the outside world interferes with the cell's homoeostasis, producing death – no more biological self-ordering phenomena from that cell. Perhaps the reason mainstream science did not recognize self-ordering phenomena for many years is precisely because they are so sensitive to interference.

This brings us back to the spontaneous origin of life in the Archaean period. There is no working hypothesis as to what this self-ordering phenomenon consisted of. It could start with genetic chemicals such as DNA or RNA, for example, or it could start with proteins or it could start with both. If there was a self-ordering phenomenon, then some reaction occurred which generated the vital autocatalyst of the system. The autocatalyst is a chemical that catalyzes the system or amplifies the reaction into a self-ordering phenomenon. Whatever hypothesis is advanced about such a self-ordering phenomenon, there must be a molecule produced which acts as the self-ordering parameter or autocatalyst. If no autocatalyst is produced, chemical reactions are incapable of doing interesting and complex things.

In an Archaean environment, there is no conceivable way of protecting the self-ordering parameter from interference by other chemicals. The Archaean was closer to a polluted toxic dump than anything else. We just can't exclude all the free radicals produced by radiation, metals, acids, halogens, and a host of others from the reaction. It is highly probable some chemical species will interfere with the all-critical amplifying component of the self-ordering phenomenon. If this were not the case, then science would take seriously the notion of cleaning up toxic dumps and other environmental problems with self-ordering systems, and for good reasons no serious research is being conducted in this field. And one is bound to observe that cleaning a toxic dump is a rather trivial problem when compared to the origin of life.

For the sake of argument, let us allow for a moment that there may have been some extraordinarily unique set of circumstances in the early Archaean which permitted the required self-ordering event or events to occur. Obviously, the gene-directed living cell is both the continuation and the final outcome of these self-ordering events. For a self-ordering phenomenon to occur, the system must be kept out of balance by a continuous flow of energy into it. The flow of energy can be viewed as the constraint – it stops the system from returning to balance or equilibrium. If we remove the constraint or the flow of energy, then the self-ordering phenomenon must collapse.

New phases of order can be derived out of chaos if there is a continuous flow of energy or matter for the new phase to feed on. The new ordered phase consumes energy so as to perpetuate its existence. With regard to the origin of life, the flow of energy comes from the sun. Thus the physical self-ordering system that camouflages itself as life is being driven by the sun's energy.

If the sun's flow of energy is cut off, will all the gene-directed life on Earth collapse back into equilibrium with the physical environment? Would all life on Earth collapse? We can conduct a thought experiment on this question. Would it be possible for humanity at some time to construct a biosphere, like an underground city, fuelled by nuclear power, in which people could cultivate plants and husband a selection of animals for their food supply? In theory, at least, we must answer in the affirmative. And so it might be said that all life does not have to perish as called for by the nature of a self-ordering event.

This thought experiment appears to confound the self-ordering system hypothesis. Self-ordering phenomena can only exist in open systems. There must be a continuous flow of energy and matter into the system to keep it far from equilibrium. If life is really only a physical self-ordering system, then when we close the system it must collapse. In the hypothetical biosphere no energy or material is flowing into the system. Instead, human intelligence is being used to transform matter into energy, but the system is still closed. What this means is that the original physical self-ordering system, as represented by life, has evolved into a state of autonomy, as represented by human beings. But this means that human intelligence is now irreducible to first principles. And thus, the philosophy of reductionism has broken down: it cannot entertain an irreducible entity.

When I applied Boltzmann's formulation of the second law, I suggested that the ever-increasing levels of organization and complexity generated by evolution could be explained if an outside source of information were available to the system. What has happened with self-ordering systems is that one of the products of evolution, humanity, has itself become knowing or intelligent. Human intelligence can supply the all-important information for survival in the hypothetical biosphere. It is always the necessity of information and intelligence that finally undermines the reductionist position.

The Second Law of Thermodynamics and Photosynthesis

I now want to discuss a final weakness of what reductionist philosophy implies about the genesis of life (though the discussion is rather complex and carries on for some time). This weakness deals with the second law of thermodynamics, and the phenomenon of photosynthesis that I have already discussed in several other contexts, earlier on.

Of great practical importance, the second law of thermodynamics states that any given process will have only one spontaneous direction: the reverse direction may not occur spontaneously. Therefore, the second law predicts the direction that natural processes take. We cannot build a ship to take up ocean water, extract energy from the water to drive the ship forward, and return the energy-depleted water to the ocean. This process does obey the first law of thermodynamics, which states that energy must be conserved, but it violates the second. Thus, when we are looking at natural processes, they all have a spontaneous direction.

All chemical and biological systems exhibit the properties of irreversibility through time. In the real world this concept of a direction is the great predictor of a reaction. To go in the opposite direction we have to force the process by doing work: it is not spontaneous. Often an appeal to common experience is used to illustrate the second law. Hot coffee, for example, cools spontaneously to the background temperature. Cold coffee never spontaneously heats up appreciably above the ambient temperature by absorbing energy from the surroundings. Similarly, in the energy of motion, a car can be brought to a halt by applying friction to the wheels through the brakes which, of course, become hot in the process. However, the car cannot be set in motion by applying heat to the brakes.

Design is a process whereby simple components are assembled together or synthesized in a very orderly manner, so as to form a new whole that exhibits deliberately intended complex behaviour. Machines are the quintessential example of design. The parts are simple while the assembled whole is complex, and the machine produces deliberately controlled non-spontaneous outcomes. If we look at a spontaneous reaction, such as a forest fire, we are simply witnesses to the spontaneous and uncontrolled combustion of wood. Much of modern humanity's technology rests on our ability to harness the energy of combustion or fire. The difference is that we control the outcome as best we can. Burning gas to power the engine of a car is infinitely more controlled than just letting it burn away spontaneously in open air. It requires design and technology to control the spontaneity of the chemical reaction so as to have a desired outcome.

The more control we exert, the greater the technology. The difference between a nuclear bomb and a nuclear reactor is we control the rate and quantity of nuclear fission in the reactor, while the bomb prompts an uncontrolled nuclear chain reaction. There is substantially more technology involved in designing and running a nuclear power plant than in making and setting off a nuclear bomb. Often non-spontaneous reactions are forced by supplying energy and catalysts. This deliberate and sequenced restraint on the spontaneity of physical processes is the hallmark of human intelligence as applied to technology. One thing is absolutely unequivocal: human technology promotes processes which could never occur spontaneously. Yet, each step of the process involved obeys the second law of thermodynamics, faithfully. In the world of science, the only places we find controls on spontaneity are in the life processes. Indeed, biological controls are analogous but greatly superior to the controls on spontaneity exhibited by human technology.

In biological metabolism, energy is first absorbed in large chunks, such as glucose, and this energy is stripped off in a sequence of very controlled steps. What should be a very spontaneous reaction – say, the oxidation of sugar – turns out to be highly controlled. Next, the energy is stored in special molecules known as adenosine triphosphate (ATP), which acts like a molecular chemical battery. Storage of useful energy is very non-spontaneous, as is evident in designing an electrical car, where the critical problem is to provide it with a sufficient store of energy in the battery. Next, this energy is used to construct large complex molecules out of small, simple molecules – another very non-spontaneous operation. In photosynthesis, energy from the sun is captured and transformed into electrical energy and then stored as chemical energy (a supremely non-spontaneous process). Virtually all biochemical processes exhibit controls on their natural spontaneity. Control is a characteristic of life. Control is also a characteristic of design. Yet again the intimation of an intelligence behind the operation of biological life is virtually inescapable.

The fundamental step in life from the standpoint of energy was to be able to harness the sun's energy with photosynthesis, and, as Manfred Eigen has explained, the efficiency of this quite amazing photosynthesizing process does approach perfection.[16] It is this one process alone which gave life autonomy on our planet: for the sun is the only constant source of energy available.

The ability of life to tap the energy flow of the sun is either a majestic piece of evolutionary good fortune or an act of deliberate design.

Ultimately, photosynthesis needs a source of hydrogen and carbon atoms. The largest single source of available hydrogen is water, which is composed of two hydrogen atoms for every oxygen atom. The technological problem is easily stated. The oxygen in water has a pretty tight grip on the electrons belonging to the hydrogens. This means that the hydrogen atoms are firmly anchored to the oxygen and we see evidence of this everyday: water is a stable molecule which shows no visible tendency to disintegrate into its constituent atoms. Then the hydrogen atoms are added to carbon dioxide, the source of carbon atoms, to form more complex molecules, such as sugar. The oxygen which is left over from the water is expelled as waste. The process is highly complex, while the concept is relatively simple.

As I have alluded to in other contexts earlier on, the importance of photosynthesis can hardly be overstated. Without it, life would have ground to a halt in a short time and there never would have been complex organisms. From the standpoint of physical science, photosynthesis is the energy cornerstone of the life process. Because it concerns energy and chemical reactions, it is entirely amenable to treatment by thermodynamics. Every year, photosynthesis harnesses vast quantities of solar energy. Estimates for the capacity of the process come in at around 500 billion tons of sugar per year and this may be an underestimation. A fraction of this energy has been preserved as coal, oil, and all the other carbonaceous materials in our rocks. This process has continued, unabated, for over 3 billion years. It has literally tamed the planet and prepared it for advanced life by transforming the atmosphere into an oxygen-rich gas. All of our free oxygen in the atmosphere is due to this one biological process. Photosynthesis counterbalances all the reactions consuming oxygen on the face of the Earth. That there is a balance is a measure of the magnitude of the photosynthesis process.

In effect, photosynthesis reverses the spontaneity of the chemical reactions which give us water and carbon dioxide. It is the source of both energy and carbon for the biological world. At the same time, it releases prodigious quantities of oxygen into the atmosphere, hence paving the way for advanced multicellular organisms. Oxidation and reduction is one of the fundamental types of chemical reaction, where the loss of electrons in a reaction is oxidation and the gain is reduction. The element oxygen is a natural oxidizer while carbon is a good reducer. Photosynthesis oxidizes oxygen and reduces carbon (a completely counter-intuitive and unexpected chemical reaction). Organisms use up oxygen and expel carbon dioxide while photosynthesis does the reverse, thus recycling the elements for reuse. And so photosynthesis is the engine of life: and yet again we are prompted to reflect on the design or coincidence equation.

Photosynthesis was either designed by some Creator or it happened naturally. And if it happened naturally, then there should be no problem from the standpoint of the second law of thermodynamics: all steps should faithfully follow the law. If it happened by the design of some Creator, one would expect that some part of the process could not proceed by spontaneous chemical reactions because an infinite entropy barrier was involved. Human technology procures non-spontaneous reactions by introducing a stage along the chemical reaction path that could not occur spontaneously.

Diamonds, for example, are found naturally in kimberlite pipes that show evidence of having been buried at great depth, thus producing very high pressure and temperature conditions, whereas carbon at the surface of the Earth forms graphite spontaneously. At the surface of the Earth the spontaneous direction for the carbon crystals is for the diamond to turn into graphite, and never the other way around. But we have devised plants which produce industrial diamonds at the face of the Earth by generating the required pressures, and so forth. There is no violation of the second law here, since the 'machinery' of the diamond plants is non-spontaneous to begin with. But spontaneously generating diamond would create havoc in the laws of chemistry and physics. We would literally have a process that is going spontaneously in both directions – and this is exactly what is prohibited by the second law of thermodynamics.

The second law does not tell us when a reaction will take place, how long it will take, whether it will go to completion, what path it will take, or whether it will go at any appreciable speed at all. What it does tell is the direction a reaction will proceed if it occurs spontaneously. Again, we can take the case of diamond for illustration. Just because the spontaneous direction is for diamond to turn into graphite does not mean the change will occur at an appreciable speed. All it tells you is that if change is to occur, diamond will turn into graphite and not the reverse. It does not matter in the slightest what path the reaction actually takes as long as everything is spontaneous. This in essence is one of the most powerful facets of the second law: we don't *need* to know the reaction path.

The reaction of hydrogen and oxygen is spontaneous whether it takes place in sunlight or in the dark: and thus the spontaneity of this reaction retains a constant direction. The product of the reaction remains stable under sunlight. Thus no matter what the conditions of the ancient Earth, the spontaneity of this reaction holds. If we were to cover the Earth with a hypothetical surface, just before life emerged over 4 billion years ago, we would have a clearly defined system with a constant flow of the sun's energy into it. Sometime between then and 3.5 billion years ago, the chemical processes of photosynthesis arose and have been maintained ever since. This is the black-box approach. We don't *need* to know the details of the genesis of life: they are all in our black box, so to speak. All we care about is the chemical reaction of oxygen and hydrogen to form water. When we approach it this way we are witness to a chemical reaction going to completion spontaneously in both directions.

It is important to remember that photosynthesis counterbalances all the oxygen-consuming reactions on the face of the planet. As an analogy, one can imagine a gigantic lake on a sunny day, where in one-half all the water is spontaneously freezing to ice, and in the other half all the ice is spontaneously melting into water. When the two halves have reached their end point they just spontaneously reverse their directions simultaneously. That is, of course, completely impossible: the water will either freeze to ice or the ice will melt to water, but the two cannot go altogether to completion simultaneously. It is likewise for the spontaneous reaction of hydrogen and oxygen to form water.

If a chemical process is proceeding to completion in both directions, then there is a great discontinuity in the experiment, and this infers an infinite entropy barrier has been crossed. Spontaneous processes cannot cross infinite entropy barriers. We know the reaction of oxygen and hydrogen is naturally spontaneous, and thus we can say that the photosynthesis process actually does cross an infinite entropy barrier. This cannot happen by itself: there has to be outside intervention – a source of information. Intelligently designed machinery has to be placed somewhere along the pathway of the reaction process. The source of the crossing of this infinite entropy barrier is the molecular machine of life itself. And thus we can conclude life could not have arisen spontaneously, because if it had photosynthesis would then be spontaneous. Then we would have to allow a chemical reaction to go to completion in both directions – and this would mean that the second law of thermodynamics is invalid.[17]

Viewed in this light, either the second law is correct or reductionist theory is correct. They cannot both be correct. This alternative approach to the thermodynamics of the spontaneous origin of life also confirms the conclusion obtained from Boltzmann's probability approach. Both applications of the second law call for a discontinuity in the origin of life. The self-ordering system fails because human intelligence is irreducible: Darwinist (or any other) reductionism is not entitled to call upon far-from-equilibrium reactions to escape the standard predictions of the second law. In this context we must conclude that the initial conditions of the Archaean waters could not have led to the spontaneous origin of life, because this would require crossing an infinite entropy barrier. My position, in other words, is that to reconcile the origin of life to the second law we are forced to introduce an intelligence variable into the equation. It is intelligence that introduced the machinery of the living cell so as to allow for the oxidation of oxygen and the reduction of carbon in the photosynthesis process.

In the end, in my view, all the currently extant scientific *evidence* supports the conclusion that the origin of life was discontinuous with respect to its initial physical environment in Archaean waters. Here is just a partial short-list of some of the key problems:

(1) Gene-based biological evolution is the most complex and systematic ordering process ever discovered by humankind. There is a scientific void as to what process could account for the emergence of the first gene-directed living cell from inanimate molecules.

(2) A living cell is such a complex entity that it has never been reassembled in a test tube. Our greatest biochemists have all failed to rebuild a cell from the exact components. Years of lab failure carry a lot of weight.

(3) The Archaean environment was extremely hostile. It was contaminated with multiple reactive chemical species, including free radicals, and constantly bombarded by high energy light. The prognosis for the survival of large pure molecules was poor to non-existent.

(4) Achieving homoeostasis is a prerequisite for life. It is intimately tied to developing a membrane. The probability of the spontaneous origin of life is tied to the availability of the prebiotic membranes. There exists no working hypothesis on how the genes coded for proteins that construct and maintain a giant fat molecule.

(5) The molecules of life are surprisingly pure compounds. There exists no working hypothesis as to how pure compounds were synthesized in the contamination of the Archaean. There is no means of assembling all the pure compounds together where they could synthesize the essential molecules of life.

(6) Proteins are built out of left-handed amino acids. Outside of life there is no natural means of separating left- and right-handed amino acids.

(7) The genetic system is formed by pure nucleotides that form a large right-handed double helix. Before a genetic system is of any use, whatsoever, it needs to be nearly structurally perfect so as to avoid an avalanche of errors. There is no means of synthesizing nucleotides naturally; they dissociate more quickly than they can be formed by chance.

(8) When reacting amino acids, there is no natural way of protecting the peptide bond. Other bonds are just as likely to form, thus destroying the useful-

ness of any proto-protein.

(9) When forming proteins with amino acids, there exists an unlimited number of ways for generating a useless protein as against a useful protein. All useful proteins would be entirely lost in a process that formed proteins without direction.

(10) Living systems require synchronized proteins. The improbabilities of generating a battery of proteins without direction are numbers with thousands of zeros in them. Synchronizing the genes with the proteins is the greatest improbability of them all.

(11) The findings of modern science are that only living things give rise to other living things. This is corroborated by the irreversibility of biological death. The spontaneous origin of life runs counter to both these characteristics of life.

(12) The logic of life rests on the great cyclical engine driven by photosynthesis. Any suggestion that inanimate molecules could evolve into a less complex organism than a photosynthesizing bacterium is inconsistent with the logic of present-day life. Any such simple bacterium would have to starve. There is no possibility that inanimate molecules could evolve directly into photosynthesizing bacteria – the entire process is orders of magnitude too complex. Even the suggestion that simple life-forms could have existed runs counter to the evidence of modern science.

(13) Because of the fundamental nature of self-ordering systems, human intelligence is irreducible. Therefore, self-ordering systems cannot account for the *origin* of life.

(14) The living cell is the most complex entity ever to have evolved. Evolution of complexity requires time. The fossil evidence indicates there is just not enough time available at all to facilitate the evolution of the first cell.

(15) The emergence of the first living cell was a singular event. With it came an extravagant evolutionary potential. There is an absence of life on the other planets. It is scientifically inconsistent to say that life is a natural derivative of inanimate chemical systems.

(16) Two independent applications of the second law of thermodynamics imply that, when all is said and done, a spontaneous origin of life is impossible. This result calls for an intelligence factor to reconcile the impossibility.

While this list is by no means complete, it constitutes an avalanche of evidence against the spontaneous-origin-of-life hypothesis. To me, the unavoidable implication is that the origin of life represents a discontinuity with the physical environment that is its home.

SUMMING-UP AND MOVING ON, AGAIN

The cornerstone of reductionism is the hypothesis that life arose spontaneously from inorganic atoms and molecules. This is the most fundamental reduction of them all and if it does not hold, traditional Darwinist philosophy is in some trouble. The fact that all life shares the same fundamental chemistry at the level of the cell implies that the origin of life was a unique event. A unique event by its very nature cannot offer compelling scientific reasons for reducing the first living cell back to atoms and molecules in the first place. The reductionist hypothesis reduces to an axiom or a statement of belief (or, for that matter, even blind faith).

Reductionism fails to explain how to reconcile life's inordinately accurate copying system and its ability to evolve. Reductionism cannot comply with the logical energy equation of life that demands photosynthesis, since this is too complex. It cannot offer a transition phase of life, since simple life-forms do not exist and would, in any case, starve if they emerged without photosynthesis. We have reviewed numerous problems that must be overcome in the spontaneous-origin-of-life hypothesis. None of them, as yet, can be resolved. All of them combined are simply refractory to reductionist explanations. The concept of a self-ordering system does have some theoretical virtues. Yet in the Archaean environment in which life must have originated, there is no conceivable way of protecting a self-ordering system from interference. Because a self-ordering system requires a constant flow of energy to keep it far from equilibrium, we can use a thought experiment to show how human intelligence cannot be reduced. The spontaneous-origin-of-life hypothesis remains an act of faith.

Biogenesis is an accepted principle of science: only living things can give rise to other living things. There is no evidence that this principle has been or could be broken in the origin of life. The default hypothesis must be that life derived from some vital force: yet science can find no evidence of a vital force in the physical universe. And, whatever else one might think, this does imply a powerful case for some 'living' extra-universal Creator.

Gene-based biological evolution is the most complex and systematic process ever discovered. Life had an origin, and whatever gave rise to the gene-directed first cell is the cause of all biological evolution. We can similarly deduce that the origin of life is the supreme ordering event. Since no genes already exist to do the ordering, we are consequently looking for some as yet unknown ordering phenomenon. To account rationally for how the complex ordering in gene-based biological evolution came about, there must be some explanation for the non-gene-directed ordering that leads to the origin of life. Yet science has no ordering phenomenon greater than biological evolution. A vacuum exists in the natural explanation of the origin of life. Vacuums want to be filled. We need some intelligent Designer to complete our account of the genesis of life.

Human technology is characterized by controls on spontaneity. And thus we arrive at an inference that controlled spontaneity implies intelligence. All life processes use controls in their functions. And thus the first life process must have been highly controlled in its functions. In particular, the first living cell must have achieved homoeostasis – a most complex and formidable accomplishment. The oldest unambiguous fossil remains of life are the stromatolites in Australia. They were produced by photosynthesizing bacteria. The entire logic of life's energy equations requires photosynthesis. Put together, all the evidence is coalescing around the notion that the first living cell was a photosynthesizing bacterium. And again, an initial organism of such complexity can only be explained by inferring an intelligent Designer.

Because the reaction of oxygen and hydrogen to form water goes to completion, the process of photosynthesis lends itself to a straightforward thermodynamic analysis. This analysis shows that the process could not occur spontaneously. There must be a discontinuity somewhere, and of course this turns out to be the origin of life. Analysis by mathematical statistics and statistical thermodynamics all confirm the sheer discontinuity of the origin of life itself. All of these results are consistent with the inference of an intelligent Designer who can set up initial conditions that remove the violation of the second law.

The genes that the first organism arrived with are the prerequisite for all future evolution. Amazingly, individual cells are turning over rapidly but life survives after 3.5 billion years, as vital as ever. This implies inordinate levels of accuracy in the copying mechanism of life. Over the same time frame, life has simultaneously evolved magnificently. A correction system in the genes is required to reconcile these two observations. Moreover, the evolution of complexity takes time and in this respect the first cell appeared remarkably early in geological history. Biological time is magnified by the irreversibility of biological death and this, in effect, catalyzes the evolution of complexity. Biological systems are designed to evolve. The genes themselves are a preadaptation for all future evolution. They are consistent with forethought in the origin of life.

Yet photosynthesis is also a prerequisite for evolution. No complex multicellular organisms could have evolved without a supply of free oxygen. Photosynthesis is the process that not only recycles carbon and provides the energy needs of life, it also tamed the planet for future organisms. Thus photosynthesis is integrally tied to the complex and systematic ordering of the evolutionary process. It offers still more compelling evidence of forethought in evolution as well. And it is the sheer scale of the forethought that is most impressive. Life begins on Earth armed with photosynthesis, not only to survive but also to tame the planet in time. Photosynthesizing bacteria went to work laying the groundwork for the great evolutionary event of multicellularity that lay 3 billion years ahead in the future.

The intellectual achievement of designing a machine which keeps running for over 3.5 billion years, that tames the planet and prepares it so that the genes within the machine can grow and produce all living things, and even an intelligent living thing, befits a Creator of the universe. Thus a belief in a Creator may move from an act of faith to an intellectual conviction about the most rational explanation for the natural order and origin of life. And, with this provocative thought in mind, the next and final stage on our trail is to explore the all-important genes, which came into the world with the origin of life for which the Creator lit the spark.

1 D. Dennett, *Darwin's Dangerous Idea: Evolution and the Meaning of Life,* (New York: Simon and Shuster, 1995) 156.

2 Ibid., 205.

3 Ibid., 157n.

4 As an earth scientist, I have found the scientific research in the area of life's origins altogether frustrating. Since an inorganic origin to life of necessity entails dealing with physical systems first and then showing how they develop into living systems, I was disappointed to find so little work dealing with the real Archaean or very early environments on earth.

   As I've already alluded to in my introduction to this book, the Archaean presents two very difficult challenges for the spontaneous origin of life. The first is the problem of contamination. While it is most probable that the necessary molecular building blocks for life could arise in Archaean environments, so, too, could a vast array of other materials. How does one prevent the vast majority of chemical species from reacting with the 'target' species? I have found virtually no discussion anywhere about how to get around this problem: from the perspective of an earth scientist, it is *the* problem, and reductionists (and almost everyone else) appear to have ignored it.

   The second related problem is concentration. Chemical reactions can only proceed if there is a sufficient concentration. How precisely were the target chemical species brought together so that they could conjure up a living cell? Again, I have failed to uncover much serious discussion on this subject.

   Both these earth-science objections are supported by theory. The second law of thermodynamics states that systems will tend to more probable states of disorder than order. Chaotic mixtures are infinitely more probable than mixtures of the pure building blocks of life. And it is in this context that the current reductionist mainstream of work in this area seems to me a form of 'sanitized' science. At present, in any event, the available literature offers only the broadest and most general outline of the spontaneous origin of life: details are extremely hard to find. Interested readers of the following suggested (and other relevant) material ought to bear this in mind.

R. Shapiro, *Origins: A Skeptic's Guide to the Creation of Life on Earth* (New York: Summit Books, 1986) is by far the best book I have read on the general subject. Shapiro does mention some and hint at other unreal scenarios typically postulated in more recent debate. A. Oparin, *Life: Its Nature, Origin and Development* (New York: Academic Press, 1964) is a somewhat older study that still has real interest. Oparin, along with Haldane, was responsible for the so-called 'pre-life-organic-soup' hypothesis. S. Miller and L. Orgel, *The Origins of Life on Earth* (Englewood Cliffs: Prentice-Hall, 1974) will repay some attention as well. Stanley Miller's experiments started a new research endeavour, which in my own view has only strengthened the case for a non-spontaneous origin of life.

Some readers may also be interested in geochemical texts, just to get a flavour of the problems an open environment presents for the spontaneous origin of life. V. Goldschmidt, *Geochemistry* (Oxford: Oxford University Press, 1954) is a classical treatment of the subject, much of which is still highly relevant. Three other useful publications are B. Mason, *Principles of Geochemistry* (New York: Wiley, 1966); H. Jeffreys, *The Earth* (Cambridge: Cambridge University Press, 1970); and J. Schopf (ed.), *Earth's Earliest Biosphere* (Princeton: Princeton University Press, 1983).

5   See F. Crick, *Life Itself: Its Origins and Nature* (New York: Simon and Shuster, 1981). Crick and Watson received the Nobel prize for their work in discovering the DNA double helix.

6   Sir F. Hoyle and N. Wickramasinghe, *Evolution from Space* (London: J.M. Dent. 1981). Fred Hoyle is a distinguished British astronomer.

7   The recent excitement concerning a reputed Martian meteorite that may indicate life on Mars 3 to 4 billion years ago is inconclusive on its own. Further exploration of the planet is required. It is worth noting that earthbound geologists have extreme difficulty in positively identifying fossil bacteria in Archaean or very old rocks on our own planet. And it is surprising that a three-pound rock sample from Mars should be considered to be so conclusive by some scientists. Enthusiasm is commendable, but so is prudence. We will all be better informed after the next exploration of the 'red planet.'

8   A fine overview of this and other theories is available in Shapiro, *Origins* (noted above). Interested readers might also want to consult Miller's own book, which is noted above as well.

9   A subject I have glossed over is the amount of radiation coming from the sun. In its earliest days, the sun is believed to have just glowed and the radiation has been increasing ever since. I believe the best-case scenario for reductionism is to have the sun as the major source of energy (though of course I may be mistaken). If the major energy sources were volcanic activity and radioactive decay, then the Archaean environment would have been even more contaminated than even I am suggesting.

10 I use the term 'far from equilibrium' here to denote the necessary conditions for the development of a self-ordering system. Self-ordering phenomena are not possible when the system is in equilibrium: it needs to be driven well out of equilibrium by the continuous flow of energy or matter into it so as to generate the far-from-equilibrium conditions necessary for self-ordering to occur. See S. Kauffman, *The Origins of Order: Self-Organization and Selection in Evolution* (London: Oxford University Press, 1993), and *At Home in the Universe: The Search for Laws of Self-Organization* (London: Oxford University Press, 1995); G. Nicolis and I. Prigogine, *Exploring Complexity: An*

Introduction (New York: W.H. Freeman, 1987); and I. Prigogine and I. Stengers, *Order out of Chaos: Man's New Dialogue with Nature* (Toronto: Bantam Books, 1984).

11 Here is a short list of phosphate minerals (most of the elements in which were readily available in the Archaean environment): Amblygonite – lithium aluminum phosphate, $Li(F,OH)AlPO_4$; Apatite – Calcium fluo-phosphate and chloro-phosphate, $Ca_5(F,Cl)(PO_4)_3$; Autunite – hydrous phosphate of calcium and uranium, $Ca(UO_2)_2(PO_4)_2$ .10-12H_2O; Libethenite – hydrous copper phosphate, $4CuO.P_2O_5.H_2O$; Phosphochalcite – hydrous copper phosphate, $6CuO.P_2O_5.3H_2O$; Pyromorphite – chloro-phosphate of lead, $Pb_5Cl(PO_4)_3$; Torbernite – hydrous phosphate of copper and uranium, $Cu(UO_2)_2(PO_4)_3.12H_2O$; Vivanite – hydrous iron phosphate, $Fe_3(PO_4)_2.8H_2O$.

This is not a comprehensive list, but it serves to illustrate the nature of the problem of 'sanitized' science. Nearly all of the combining minerals were readily available in the Archaean environment, but no noticeable concentration of these minerals has ever been reported. As I alluded to in the introduction to this book, we also now know that many of the ore deposits of the Archaean were syngenetic in nature; i.e., they were contemporaneous with the formation of the rocks that host them: we can think of them as chemical precipitates. Scientists have to dream up some very unique set of conditions which will both preclude the formation of phosphate minerals and provide a source of phosphorous for the prebiotic synthesis of living cells.

The essential point is that once we determine what these conditions could be, they represent the set of possible conditions. If we were to do the same for each of the building blocks of life, then we would be able to determine whether any range of conditions could have existed where the formation of life *could* have taken place. Once we have these ranges, we can conduct our experiments under these conditions and no other. Neither reductionist nor any other partisans to the great debate have made any serious effort to tackle this task, largely because, I believe, it represents a practical impossibility.

Some interested readers might want to consult two sources on phosphate minerals: W. Deer, R. Howie, and J. Zussman,. *Rock-Forming Minerals* (New York: Wiley, 1962), v.5; and H. Read, *Rutley's Elements of Mineralogy* (26th edition, London: Thomas Murby & Co., 1970).

12 H. Bergson, *Creative Evolution* (Lanham: University Press of America, 1911).

13 In a related context, it has always intrigued me that living organisms only metabolize right-handed sugars. Presumably when the first cell evolved, it would have metabolized right-handed sugars, but this surely left open a wonderful opportunity for an organism to evolve the ability to metabolize left-handed sugars. Yet it has not happened.

14 See Prigogine's and Kauffman's works cited above.

15 For a much more extensive account, see Prigogine and Stengers, *Order out of Chaos*.

16 See Dennett, *Darwin's Dangerous Idea*, 163.

17 Behe offers both photosynthesis and electron transport chains as examples of irreducibly complex systems, and his work corroborates my analysis here on the microscopic level. See M. Behe, *Darwin's Black Box: The Biochemical Challenge to Evolution* (New York: The Free Press, 1996), 160.

CHAPTER 6

The Information-Based Molecular Machine

All the material of the previous four chapters logically converges on the nature of the genes. Somehow the brain is coded for by the genes. Embryology is controlled by genes. Evolution is driven by changes in the genes. The hierarchical nature of the biological classification system is a genetic master blueprint of life.

The intricate complexity of the living cell with all its chemical feedback mechanisms is under the control of the genes. We can see this in the proteins, which act as the muscles of the cell and do all the work. The composition and function of proteins is exactingly specific. All the information about specifications of the proteins is found coded in the genes. The genes are in effect a storehouse of information or non-random signals. The genes consist of a sequence of signals that can be read and transduced into the composition of the proteins. Thus we arrive at the information-based organization of the living cell that is so difficult to reduce to simple chemistry. The trick of heredity is that the genes can copy themselves.

THE COMPLEXITY OF LIFE

A chasm exists between the biological world and the physical world. Every advance in molecular biology has confirmed the absence of an intermediate state between life and non-life. Modern science confronts us with a discontinuity between life and physical chemistry. A simple bacterial cell is made up of millions of atoms and represents a level of complexity unequalled in the physico-chemical world. A cell is like a giant self-controlling chemical supermolecule. This order and complexity of life arises because life has an internal source of information. This distinguishes life from non-life and generates the chasm or discontinuity between the two. The most fundamental characteristic of life is its information content, found in the genetic code and consisting of large genetic molecules in the form of DNA or RNA. The discovery of this information base to life has created a revolution in biology. Molecular biology deciphers the genetic code in terms of control circuits and information theory.

At present, the extremes of life's complexity are represented at the lower end by bacteria and at the higher end by humanity. While the format of the genetic code in a human being and a bacterium is compatible, there is a difference in how the DNA molecules are organized in both types of organisms. E. coli is a relatively simple bacterium or prokaryote, and it or a close relative is believed to have been in existence for a billion and more years. It is found in most humans and has been extensively studied by molecular biologists. The cell has no nucleus and the DNA molecules of the genes lie in a coiled ring near the centre. Various proteins are holding it in place and enzymes are latching on and off, so that they can read the information in the sequence of molecules or bases of the DNA. Substantial amounts of the DNA, however, are uncluttered by proteins, and these features have often led to the suggestion that the DNA of bacteria is streamlined for action: the organization of the bacterial DNA affords the most rapid access to, and response from, the information in the genes.

In fungi, plants, and animals the situation is quite different. The cells of these organisms have the genetic material packaged into a nucleus which is segregated by a membrane from the rest of the cell's body. In the nucleus the DNA is packed with proteins called histones, which bend the DNA round on itself to form a larger coil. This coil in turn is folded into larger coils. The nucleus itself represents the highest level of this packing arrangement. The picture then emerges of the nucleus acting as a storage centre for a vast quantity of DNA running throughout the nucleus. The convoluted nature of the actual DNA is just a means to store all the pieces of information, similar to the way we fold large blueprints, plans, or maps.

Plasmids are short genetic sequences located in the cytoplasm of cells that usually perform specific functions. They are common in bacteria and they become increasingly more scarce in higher animals. The mammalian organization of DNA seems to preclude the independent use of circular sections of DNA as represented by the plasmids. Some plasmid-like viruses are a cause of cancer in humans. Where plasmids occur in higher organisms, such as fungi and plants, the circular DNA is 'packed' in proteins. It is a feature of the cells of higher organisms that loose DNA is either packed by proteins or broken into its constituent molecules. A low tolerance exists for loose cannons of information floating around the more complex cells.

Humans have about 750 times as much DNA as bacteria but they do not appear to have 750 times as many genes. Some frogs and newts have 10 times as much DNA as humans while the lungfish has 50 times as much. Thus it is not possible to correlate complexity and numbers of genes directly with the absolute amount of DNA. Genes of higher organisms bear the scars of their evolutionary history in the form of junk DNA, pseudogenes, and so forth. Yet one can crudely correlate the number of genes with intricacy and, with every advance in the field of biochemistry and molecular biology, living cells and organisms are seen to exhibit ever-increasing levels of sophistication. The cytoplasm of the cell at one stage was considered to be a rather uninteresting suspension giving 'fill' to the cell – a position that has been revolutionized by molecular biology.

PROTEINS

The versatility of a living cell comes about through its proteins. Proteins are the workhorses of the cell. Broadly speaking, we divide proteins into fibrous proteins and globular proteins. The fibrous variety are insoluble and are used in structural roles in the tissue. Globular proteins are used for the maintenance and regulation of the life processes. They are soluble and they include all the enzymes. The other molecules and constituents that make up the cell, such as carbohydrates, pigments, and fats, are produced and regulated by proteins or protein-controlled reaction pathways within the cell. Proteins in the form of enzymes are critical in the process of replication. The genes control and regulate the production, composition (hence design), and the operation of the proteins. Through their control of the proteins, the genes have overall control of the cell. This represents a very fundamental generalization of the organization of the cell. In short, the cell is under the control of the genes via the proteins.

Proteins are super molecules built out of amino acids. As I have already mentioned, there are 20 different essential amino acids. A protein super molecule can consist of hundreds of amino acids. The actual position and type of amino acid tends to be quite specific, although some substitution of similar amino acids can take place. We can think of the primary structure as a long, drawn-out chain of interconnected amino acids. But no protein exists as a long, drawn-out chain. As soon as the long chain is formed, it folds naturally. The way the protein folds is governed by the characteristics of the sequence of amino acids along the chain. Long chains have a number of different ways of folding and often another protein is used to guide the folding into the specific configuration.

The primary chain of amino acids in a protein can be subdivided into distinct sub-sequences. These shorter sequences have particular attributes in themselves that contribute to the overall characteristics of the proteins. The attractive and repulsive forces in each distinct sequence ensure that the primary long chain of the protein will fold in on itself in the same way every time. A substitution of one amino acid for another is only allowed if it has the same general properties as the original, and is similar in the three-dimensional function of the protein. The three-dimensional structure of the protein is its working structure. By hiding particular chemical characteristics inside the structure, and exposing other chemical properties on the outside, the proteins can develop specific attributes, such as an attraction or repulsion to water. The three-dimensional structure has a very specific shape, and it is this shape that allows proteins to perform so many of their vital functions, particularly as enzymes.

The shape of proteins consistently appears as if it came about deliberately, almost as if an engineer had designed it. Collagen is a structural protein that has the qualities of a stiff fibre with units at both ends for forming connections. The molecule comes in a triple helix and is arranged into a bundle by offsetting all the joints, so as to have no one area of weakness along a joint, and these bundles are then piled at right angles to each other to maximize strength further. Thus collagen can produce great strength and flexibility. The flexible usage of structural proteins is seen in keratin which plays a vital role in fur, feathers, scales, and claws. Elastin is another structural protein that looks like it was designed to allow for the all-important flexibility in tissues such as lungs. Proteins also form the cytoskeleton of the cell, which determines the cell shape.

Proteins have short sequences of amino acids which tell the cell where to put the proteins. Collagen, for example, is useless inside the cell because there is no requirement for reinforcement inside the cell. It has to go outside the cell to provide strength. The short sequences of proteins are known as signal peptides, and are contained at the end of the protein. The movement of proteins to their specific site of activity is an automatic process based on chemistry. One can almost think of the signal peptides as a chemical label, which will invariably go to one particular site in the cell, bringing its protein along. It is quite analogous to a postal zip code and a specific address.

There are a great number of proteins that perform regulatory functions, both in the cell itself and between the cells. Hormones carry signals from one part of the body to another distant part through the blood. The endorphins in the brain are like neurotransmitters: they are short sequences of amino acids that send signals between the cells in the brain. Animal cells have histocompatibility proteins on their outside, which function to discern the compatibility of other cells. Many regulatory proteins exist but most of these have only small concentrations: one does not need too much growth hormone to stimulate growth. Molecular biology and biochemistry are gradually generating a picture of a highly organized chemical machine inside and outside the cell. Precise specificity is to be expected for both proteins and cells themselves.

The most important function for proteins in the cell is to act as enzymes. Enzymes in general perform catalysis of particular chemical reactions and regulatory functions in the cell, and between different cells in a multicellular organism. Every enzyme has a shape tailored to the job it has to do. The enzymes are like a specialized tool with a very specifically shaped active site, so constructed that enzymes latch on to one type of target almost perfectly while other types of targets are not affected. In catalyzing a chemical reaction, the active site is constructed to fit the molecule exactly: no other shape of molecule will fit in to be catalyzed. It is believed that the left-handedness of the amino acids aids this shaping of the active site.

Enzyme specificity is the order of the day in the cell, and each process has its own enzyme. It is surprising that the proteins are not generalists in any way. Each protein performs a very specific task, usually with great efficiency and speed. Outside of its particular speciality, the protein tends to be rather useless to the economy of the cell. In the typical biological economy, however, it has often been found that a used-up protein can be broken down into smaller proteins to be used elsewhere in the cell. The more we learn about the molecular machine, the more efficient and economical it appears. Thus the cell seems rigid and inflexible in manufacturing specific tools for every task in its operation, but this is just a measure of the order within the cell. And this cellular order contrasts with the comparative chaos of human organization where versatility is a virtue.

A battery of enzymes can put molecules together or pull them apart with incredible efficiency. It is enzymes that allow the cell to break down large molecules for energy requirements: each metabolic pathway, consisting of a long series of synchronized reactions, is a maze of complexity and order. Enzymes enable cells to build large molecules out of smaller ones, and it is this ability to synthesize that really characterizes biological life. The building of larger molecules out of smaller molecules is an uphill struggle that requires a constant supply of energy. The entire cell with all of its complexity and order runs automatically: it is self-contained with regard to its own operations. All automatic systems have to have a control centre, and in the cell the control centre is in the genes.

I have tried to convey here the remarkable order that is emerging from molecular biology. It seems a very reasonable hypothesis that everything has a purpose in the economy of the cell. The cell puts proteins together in a specific composition. It turns out that this composition determines the all-important structure of the three-dimensional configuration of the protein. One of the mysteries of life is how the chemical composition of a protein and its eventual function are related. Molecular biologists have been unable to design and specify the amino acid sequence of new proteins. Since the majority view is that proteins must have arisen spontaneously, this is somewhat surprising. Nothing impresses me more than the precise and specific function of a protein. One thing is absolutely clear: no protein gradually worked its way into the job. It takes some time to digest the fact that the proteins are packed off to specific locations in the cell. This means that function and location have all been coded for in the DNA of the genes. And the ultimate question is: how do the genes know about everything?

THE GENETIC CODE AND PROTEIN SYNTHESIS

To begin looking at the synthesis of a protein we have to start with the genetic code. All living cells in nature have a similarity in design vis-a-vis the roles of DNA, RNA, and protein. The proteins do all the work of the cell but they are ultimately under the control of the genes or DNA. The genes are the brains of the operation while the proteins are the muscle. In developing a taxonomy, we can start with genes and divide the world into those things that have DNA or RNA and reproduce, and those that don't. Once we classify the world in this fashion we find that there are no transitional states between life and physical chemistry available for study. Though science is full of discontinuities, there is probably no other simple classification rule that so completely generates a discontinuity or chasm in the world of nature.

DNA is the molecular material that makes up the genetic system of all living things. The ultimate trick of DNA is that it can duplicate itself. Imagine, for instance, that the DNA molecule is a ladder and that we are going to build this ladder. A ladder consists of two long pieces and the connecting rungs. To build the long pieces we will fasten sugar molecules together by means of a phosphate. Suppose now that we have built the left and right long pieces of the ladder out of these sugars and phosphates. We are going to build the rungs of the ladder out of four molecules, usually known as bases, that are called Adenine, Guanine, Thymine, and Cytosine (or A,G,T, and C for short). But each single base can only form half a rung. We have to put two of them together to form a full rung. The connections between A,G,T, and C are like a male-female arrangement.[1] In this arrangement, A is a large male and G is an equally large female, while T is a small female and C is a small male. There is only one way of keeping the rungs all the same length. We have to pair A with T and G with C. If we don't keep to this rule, the rungs will be unequal, and this is not allowed. Now on the left long piece of the ladder we can attach any sequence of these bases we choose – there is no restriction. Suppose that the sequence is A,A,G,T,C ... at least to start.

When we come to assemble the right side we find we have no latitude or freedom at all. Opposite A we must put T; opposite G we must put C; opposite T we must put A; opposite C we must put G; and on it goes like this. It turns out that the left and right halves of the ladder are precise compliments of each other. The usefulness of this complementarity can be shown quickly. Disassemble the ladder down the middle into left and right halves again, so that the left half has a string of single bases on it and the right half has the complimentary half on it. By introducing two new long pieces which are standard equipment, so to speak, and a new supply of bases, we can construct two identical ladders that are an exact match of the original. In this way our DNA ladder is capable of copying itself – the ultimate trick of heredity. This allows a cell to copy all of its information so as to produce two identical cells. Of course any particular shorter sequence can be copied faithfully as well. And if we now twist right-handedly the long pieces of our ladder, we have the famous double helix of DNA.

The genetic information is contained in the exact sequence of bases along one chain. Because of the pairing of the bases, the genetic information is actually recorded twice or in complimentary form. Genes are a sequence of subunits in the DNA molecule that act as a coded message. Thus the sequence of bases A,G,T, and C in the DNA of the gene is the code for the specification of a protein at its most simple. In the case of synthesizing a protein, the key point to appreciate is that the bases are arranged in triplets. There are only four bases and therefore there must be four-times-four-times-four possible triplets or 64 triplets in all. Most triplets stand for a particular amino acid but, incredibly enough, there are punctuation triplets for start and stop as well. Obviously if there are 60-odd possible triplets and only 20 amino acids, different triplets can stand for the same amino acid.

The first step in forming a protein is to copy or transcribe the gene sequence in the DNA into a sequence of RNA known as messenger RNA.[2] On average, protein composition varies from 100 to 500 amino acids. With a ratio of three bases for each amino acid then the gene is over 300 to 1,500 bases long, and the messenger RNA has about the same variation in length. In cells with a nucleus, the initial RNA transcript of DNA must be further processed. This is necessary because genes of higher organisms usually have short sequences that interrupt the coding for protein information. These are called introns. Why introns exist is something of a mystery at present. The initial transcript copies the entire DNA sequence, introns and all. The next step is to cut out the introns. Finally, the coding sequences that are left are spliced together to form mature messenger RNA. Thus transcription entails the locating of the gene on the double helix, the opening of the helix by an enzyme to reveal one strand of DNA, the copying of the information into a strand of RNA (the actual transcription), and then the 'editing' of the RNA – by cutting out the introns and splicing together the remaining sequence to form messenger RNA.

When finally processed, the messenger RNA passes through pores in the nuclear membrane on its way to a ribosome. Ribosomes are the protein-manufacturing centres of the cell and they consist of a complex of about 50 proteins and three types of RNA. The ribosome attaches itself to the start of the messenger RNA molecule. A triplet of the bases in the messenger RNA is known as a codon, and this triplet is matched exactly by an anticodon on a special type of nucleotide called transfer RNA. Transfer RNA is a strand that is about a hundred bases long. These transfer RNAs always have an amino acid attached to them that matches for the codon exactly. This critical 'loading' of the transfer RNA is performed by yet another specialized enzyme. There is a specific enzyme for each type of transfer RNA. As the messenger RNA passes through the ribosome, the transfer RNA pick up the triplets individually, while special proteins pick up the amino acid from the transfer RNA and attach the amino acid to the growing protein chain.

Thus the protein molecule is assembled sequentially, amino acid by amino acid, each forming a chemical bond with the previous amino acid. When the chain is assembled, it detaches from the transfer RNA molecules and begins folding automatically. It appears that in many cases specialized proteins are required to guide the folding protein into the required three-dimensional shape. The protein invariably has a short peptide sequence which insures that the protein will arrive at its correct functional location in the cell. The whole process is over in seconds.

THE RIBOSOME PROBLEM AND THE ORIGIN OF LIFE

The two-stage morphology of a protein, i.e., its primary long chain and its final three-dimensional shape, causes almost insurmountable problems in generating a group of functional proteins at random.[3] It is evident that once an amino acid chain has formed, it will fold immediately, whether it is functional or not. Once it is in the folded or tertiary structure there is no way of adding amino acids to the chain, since it no longer exists. It has been transformed into a three-dimensional structure. To appreciate this further we must take account of the speed at which chemical bonds form naturally: a thousand bonds can form in seconds. To form a protein, then, every single amino acid must be at the reaction site at the same time, and they must react in the correct sequence. Once the chain is long enough it will automatically begin to fold in on itself. It takes anywhere from fractions of a second to perhaps as much as five seconds for proteins to fold into their final three-dimensional shapes.

Because of all this, the difficulty of forming a protein by random means is proportional to its length. All the problems of generating proteins at random covered in the last chapter have to be taken into account. The probability of generating a functional protein is remote in comparison to the probability of generating junk molecules. And again we seem to be left with no choice: the synthesis of a protein has to be a controlled affair, and so we turn to the genes for this control. But the genes cannot help in the synthesis of a protein without the aid of other proteins. Accurate proteins are required to synthesize accurate proteins.

The paradox of the chicken and egg has now hit with full force. No matter which path is taken, accurate proteins are needed to form accurate proteins. Which came first; the proteins or the genes? To generate an accurate protein, the information as to its exact composition is first required. This is provided for by the genes. But access to this information is only provided by means of a battery of accurate proteins that are set up so as to complete the task of transcription and assembly. There is no creeping up on the synthesis of a protein in the cell's ribosome. To synthesize any accurate protein, the battery of accurate proteins that are synchronized in their function in the ribosome is required. Where did the first accurate proteins come from? The consistent feature of molecular biology is how precise and exact is the function of each of the proteins. If we start out with inexact proteins there is no theoretical possibility that they will become more exact in time. If the ribosome does not read the codons accurately, what will it synthesize in the end? The ratio of possible useless proteins to useful ones is so great that all an inaccurate ribosome can produce is junk proteins. Denton writes:

> If translation is inaccurate, this leads in turn to a more inaccurate translational apparatus which leads inevitably to further inaccuracies, and so forth. Each imperfect cycle introduces further errors. To improve itself, such a system would have to overcome its fundamental tendency to accumulate errors in exponential fashion. The very cyclical nature of cellular replication guarantees that imperfections inexorably lead to autodestruction.[4]

Is this all starting to sound familiar? So far as the state of our knowledge today goes, the ribosome problem presents an enormous barrier to any kind of reductionist philosophy on the origin of life. One can only generate accurate proteins with the help of the genes, and one can only enlist the help of the genes in this matter with the aid of accurate proteins in the first place. This situation is impossible to resolve and many geneticists are not afraid to say so.

All the exact specifications of the biological cell trace back to the genes. The genes are the brains of the operation and the proteins are the muscles. The brains and the muscles are integrally related to each other. They form two separate parts of the same whole. If everything is to be reduced back to its chemical composition then we have to be able to reduce the chemistry of the amino acids into the chemistry of the genes. Or we could try to reduce the chemistry of the genes into the chemistry of the amino acids. To date, there exists no functional chemical relationship between the bases of DNA and the 20 amino acids. It is impossible to derive one from the other. As far as we can ascertain, the four bases of DNA could have been quite different. The challenge to any reductionist theory whatsoever is to derive the chemical logic of the genes from the amino acids, or the logic of the amino acids from the genes. We can find no reducing chemical relationship between DNA and the amino acids, and hence the proteins. We can conclude by saying that the proteins and the genes are two independent chemical systems. And this leads to a general statement of one of the most fundamental problems in the origin of life: *It is not possible to reduce the chemistry of the genes to the chemistry of the amino acids/proteins. Nor is it possible to reduce the chemistry of the amino acids/proteins to the chemistry of the genes. The genes and the amino acids/proteins are chemically independent of each other.*

This means that there is no chemical explanation of why a codon should specify a particular amino acid. Or conversely, there is no reason why an amino acid should specify a particular codon. There exists no automatic mechanism of relating the brains of the cell to the muscles. The ribosome functions as a transducer; i.e., it converts different genetic codons into different amino acids. A transducer is a device that converts a variation of one independent quantity into another independent quantity. The mechanical bridge between the two independent quantities is the transducer itself. A transducer, for example, can convert barometric pressure into electrical voltage. Under normal circumstances, these two quantities have no direct relationship to each other. As Crick has explained:

> The exact nature of the genetic code is as important for biology as Mendeleev's Periodic table of the Elements is for chemistry, but there is an important difference. The periodic Table would be the same everywhere in the universe. The genetic code appears rather arbitrary, or at least partly so. Many attempts have been made to deduce the relationship

between the two languages (proteins and nucleotides) from chemical principles but so far none have been successful. The code has a few regular features but these might be due to chance ...With the exception of the mitochondria, the code is identical in all living things so far examined, and even for mitochondria the differences are rather small. This would not be surprising if there were an obvious structural reason for the details of the code; if certain amino acids had necessarily to go with certain codons because, for example, their shapes fitted neatly together. Brave attempts have been made to suggest how this could happen, but they all seem unconvincing. It is as least as plausible that the details of the code are mainly accidental.[5]

In the last chapter we presented a selection of problems that accompany the spontaneous-origin-of-life hypothesis. Each problem in its own right is virtually insurmountable, and collectively they form a formidable obstacle to the hypothesis. Now it transpires that the coupling of the genes to the proteins is the highest level of the difficulty here. Self-ordering phenomena will not help the situation because we are compelled to couple two independent systems. And the only known factor that can couple two independent quantities together is intelligence. Confronted with nearly insurmountable scientific arguments against the spontaneous inorganic origin of life, we are forced to allow the principle of biogenesis to hold, and thus to posit the existence of another living Being to account for the origin of life on Earth. We can also conclude that this Being is characterized by intelligence, since a factor of intelligence is required to overcome the problems in thermodynamics.

This and all the evidence cited in the book so far allow us to interpret the ribosome for what it appears to be. A transducer is an artifact of intelligence. It requires intelligence to couple two independent systems. The ribosome couples the two chemically independent systems of the proteins and the genes. The ribosome is a transducer produced by an intelligent Being. Building on the base of a factor of intelligence from thermodynamics, and the intelligence required to produce a transducer, we can argue that genes have the 'nature' of a creative symbolic language – another artifact of an intelligent Being.

THE INTELLIGENCE–GENES CONNECTION

To take this argument down its final steps, in molecular biology we are constantly confronted with the logic of DNA and the chemistry of life. The logic of DNA always reduces to genes and information. The DNA molecule is full of information. The primary signal of information is in the exact sequence of the genetic codon. These primary signals are coupled together to form a secondary long signal or gene. But the genes themselves are coupled in the organization and running of the cell. In short there are multi-levelled signals in the genetic code. Information theory would allow for the random appearance of signals, but it cannot account for the precise coupling of meaningful signals by random means. It is not possible to generate information signals at random, and then apply these signals in an exact manner in an application by random means.

Either a deterministic mechanical relationship between the signal and the application is required or a transducer must be used. It has already been noted that there is no deterministic mechanical relationship between genes and proteins, and so a transducer must be used. Moreover, if one reflects on the problem, it is evident that two transducers are required, not one. The primary transducer must generate the information signal, while the secondary transducer must translate the signal in the application. The functioning of the ribosome accounts for the secondary transducer. But the primary transducer remains unaccounted for.

We have an analogue of the problem in computers, where the hardware processes information while the software embodies information. If we let the hardware represent the proteins then the software would represent the genes. One has to ask, is there any conceivable way of randomly generating a complex computer program by trial and error? It is extremely difficult to see how this could come about. Add to this the problem of generating the actual mechanical computer by trial and error. Again one has to stretch even to imagine how such an event could come about. But these problems are only trivial when compared with linking the two. How do we propose that the software can communicate with the computer? In terms of today's PCs, how do we randomly generate a disk-operating system or DOS that is both compatible to the hardware and to the software simultaneously, when we have no specifications for either the machine or the program to start with?

In theory, at least, there is an infinite number of possible languages in which to write the software instructions. Correspondingly, there is an immense number of possible machine languages, or languages which tell the machine what to do. This means that there is an infinite number of possible compilers or transducers between the two types of languages. The machine must be able to understand the program. But this also requires that the program understands the machine in the first place. (And this also illustrates the presence of the two transducers.)

The compiler functions as the secondary transducer, translating software signals into usable machine language. Nothing will happen unless the program has been designed for the machine in question. We can generate endless amounts of machine-language signals at random, but the computer will do absolutely nothing with them. There has to be a primary transduction that embodies the information to be processed, and the information that specifies the machine. Without the use of standards, conventions, and guides the probabilities of the software program and the machine ever communicating are infinitesimal. The primary transducer in computers is human intelligence, which acts to embody information into the software program. A virtually identical problem exists in the origin of life, since the first genetic signal must have had real information about the first organism embodied in it.

When we address the origin of life, the crux of the problem is that there is no deterministic mechanical chemical relationship between the proteins and the genes. Life is an information-driven system. It is this one characteristic in the form of the genetic code that separates life from non-life. The information signal of the genes is discontinuous with the activities of the proteins. The information has to be transduced in the ribosome so as to generate proteins, but there must be something to transduce in the first place: random signals will produce random proteins at the very best. The extraordinary thing about all this is that the genetic signal includes a signal for the composition and functioning of the ribosome itself. Whatever else they are, proteins are not random and ribosomes are most unrandom. The primary genetic signal of life had to incorporate information about the composition and function of proteins, and information about how to get this protein information to the proteins.

Is it possible to assemble a comprehensible chemistry textbook by randomly selecting letters from all possible languages? We could argue that the chemistry text has a unique combination of letters in the English language, and thus there must be some non-zero probability of such a thing, no matter how infinitely small it is. But this, of course, is practical nonsense: it just cannot be done. An improbability with a hundred zeros or more in it is, in practise, an impossibility. If we restrict ourselves to the vocabulary and the letters of the English language the problem is greatly simplified, but still remains practically impossible.

The use of a specific language is similar to a secondary transducer in that we now have a specific code for transmitting knowledge. But it does not mean that we have any knowledge to transmit. There is no deterministic relationship between the real world and the English language. We cannot embody knowledge about the real world in English syntax unless we already have knowledge to begin with. The intellectual activity of the human mind is the primary transducer, and random events cannot substitute for the activity of an intelligent Mind. The relationship between the proteins and the genes is quite analogous. There is no deterministic relationship between the two, so even if there was a ribosome in place nothing at all would happen. The genetic signal has to be more than a statistically non-random signal. It must incorporate true knowledge of the outside world – in this case the living cell.

A code suggests something quite invariant, rigid, and mechanically linked. Once we accept the notion of evolution, it is obvious that evolution has produced vast numbers and types of organisms with all sorts of sizes and shapes. Evolution is a characteristic of life and it is a gene-directed phenomenon. Quite clearly the genetic code is not just a rigid formula for specific instructions. Whatever else the genetic code has succeeded in doing, it most certainly has changed its instructions since every species has a discreet type of code. Every new enzyme has a specialized shape which is used almost exclusively for one purpose. Every new enzyme is preceded by a new gene.

Evolution is a characteristic of life and it can be interpreted as a creative process analogous to the creativity expressed in literature or technology. In English we start with 26 letters and 10 basic numbers, and by rules of grammar and convention we are capable of expressing (in one respect or another) all present human knowledge. We are also capable of expressing and communicating endless amounts of new knowledge, and endless new ideas and processes. There is no theoretical limit on the amount of information that can be encoded by the English language, or any other modern language. Instead, what limit there is lies in human intelligence. A language is inherently flexible because it expresses intelligent ideas, while a code is inherently rigid because it is mechanistic in nature. It is more than safe to say, I think, that the flexible nature of the genetic code is self-evident.

If we take one of the products of evolution, such as an insect, and do a comprehensive critique, it is apparent that a highly creative process went into generating the creature. I would suggest myself that the beetle (there are close to 500,000 species of beetle in existence at the moment) represents in total a far higher level of creativity than the sum of all human creativity to date. The elegance and design of the beetle's appendages exceeds by a quantum leap the combined efforts of human beings to design appendages for robots. Every aspect of each individual biological organism is virtually unrivalled by the sum of human efforts in comparable fields. Every species of organism approaches the level of perfection in its adaptation to its environment. At present, any of the species of organisms alive today, even the most simple, is infinitely beyond the intelligence and technology of humanity to mimic in the lab.

The realization that the evolutionary process has produced at least a billion creative templates of life for different species (to say nothing of absolutely inordinate numbers of individual living beings) is simply staggering. The variety of life that has manifested itself throughout geological time is a monument to the creativity of evolution. But all evolution is under the control of the genes, and thus this monument of creativity is rightly attributed to the genetic code. Human creativity is only a small subset of the totality of creativity of the genetic code itself. This amount and quality of creativity cannot be produced by a rigid mechanical code. The genetic code has to have flexible qualities similar to that of a modern language.

The genetic code is the great discriminator between life and non-life. There is no bridge between the two since viruses are produced in living cells only. This fact alone suggests that the genetic code has an indispensable quality to it that is different from anything else in the physical world. We must also take account of the stark fact that evolution has conserved the essentials of the code throughout geological time. There has been no drift in the format of the code and the functioning of the ribosome. It is a most extraordinary discovery that all biological systems are characterized by change and evolution, while the source of all the change retains an invariable format. Scientifically this situation is as counter-intuitive as one could conceive. Some very fundamental factor holds the genetic code to an invariable format.

In the production of proteins we saw that the instructions were formulated in a code of four bases arranged in letters three bases long – a codon. There is every analogue to language in the function of these codons, including stop and start punctuation. Yet because of the chemical chasm between the genetic bases and the amino acids, we are forced to conclude that the bases are operationally analogous to symbols. DOG is only related to man's best friend by convention or agreement. The letters, and indeed the word, are only symbolic. In French, the exact same meaning is achieved by CHIEN, which has no obvious functional relationship to the English version. Part of the genetic code then is made up of symbolic language used to specify proteins. Misspelling a word in English does not produce new words. It may in context produce an alternative word, but that alternative word would already have been in the language. The invariance of the format of the genetic code for living organisms flows from its symbolic qualities. Real knowledge is embodied in the symbols of the code. If the format is changed, the symbol and the embodied knowledge become divorced: the new symbol in effect stands for nothing in the real world. Thus the extreme restriction on the format of the genetic code over geological history is a result of its relationship with real knowledge. Any other format results in mere noise, without any meaning in the world of proteins and the affairs of a living cell.

The rest of the code is used for control. Genes are turned on and off by a control mechanism. The embryology of a multicellular organism, such as a human being, is the penultimate testimony for controls in the genes. The newborn baby has billions of cells, each carrying exactly the same amount of information in the genes. Each cell is differentiated in its function in the child. This differentiation is brought about by controls over what information is available to each cell. What controls the controller? Organisms are integral wholes, whether they are bacteria or human beings. Ultimately, it is some form of master program that defines this wholeness. This master program probably controls the subprograms through some form of hierarchical arrangement.

So the genetic code not only contains symbolic language but a master program, with subprograms within it and subroutines within the subprograms. Allied to this we must take account of the precise composition, structure, function, location, and synchronization of the proteins. The proteins are chemically discontinuous to the genetic code, but they are precisely coded for symbolically by the same genetic code. The information signals in the genes contain knowledge, but this knowledge is in an abstract form. It is literally written in a chemical language so concise that all human knowledge could easily be condensed in genetic form on a teaspoon. There is no fundamental difference between using chemical molecules as symbols and using strange-looking symbols that we call letters to write down information. And finally we must add the creative characteristic of the genetic code – evolution has generated at least a billion individual species: whatever else it may be, this code *is* a creative language.

The essentials of the entire being of the beetle are found in abstract form in its genetic code. Similarly, the essentials of the entire being of a monkey are found in abstract form in its genetic code. The beetle code and the monkey code are similar in appearance and form. So, too, a romance novel and a legal textbook are similar in form and appearance, but the content of the abstraction could hardly be more different. The content of the beetle's code and the monkey's code could hardly be more different either. Evidence of a creative symbolic language points once again to an Intelligence. This is why the irreducibility of the chemistry of the genes to the chemistry of the amino acids/proteins is so pivotal. There is absolute unanimity in the scientific world that the genes contain information. If this information cannot be derived mechanistically, like water forming ice at zero degrees Celsius and one atmosphere, then it must of necessity be symbolic.

The answer to the problem of assembling a chemistry text by selecting letters at random is now apparent. We are trying to abstract the real world by random processes. We cheated by introducing the secondary transducer of the letters of the English language, but still the problem was insurmountable. Abstraction is a definitive characteristic of intelligent beings. Intelligence is a higher-order phenomenon in the universe. It is impossible to mimic the higher order with elements of the lower order, such as atoms and molecules, without first transducing the intelligence. And thus the constraints on the abstraction lie in the domain of intelligence. This is where the transducer or language comes into the picture. In language we agree to certain rules and conventions. This agreement is an act of intelligence, and it cannot be mimicked by random processes or contingent events.

Of infinitely greater import still is the content of the language. We have billions of people capable of writing and doing mathematics, but only a mere handful who can raise the content to the heights of Newton or Shakespeare. And so it is with the genes as well. The genetic code abstracts all of the essentials of an organism and its individual functions in a symbolic language. The genes embody knowledge about the cell in abstract form. The ribosome transducer links the abstract information of the genes to the real-world physical function of the proteins. And there had to exist a prior Intelligence that was responsible for the abstraction, raising the content to heights that mere humanity, even with all the high technology of contemporary science in the global village, can perhaps never remotely hope to achieve.

GOD EXISTS: A SEMIFINAL SUMMING-UP

In the previous chapter, the spontaneous-origin-of-life hypothesis violated the second law of thermodynamics in two independent applications. We need an intelligence factor to explain these violations. The hypothesis runs into insurmountable problems in coupling the genes to the proteins. The ribosome problem is insoluble. The nature of the problem is that the genes and the proteins are two chemically independent systems, neither one of which can be reduced to the other. Thus there can be no self-determining link between them.

Once we accept the idea that the inorganic origin of life is impossible, the biogenesis principle must be allowed to stand: it takes a living being to generate another living being. And thus the answer to the origin of life on Earth points to another living being. The two independent systems of the proteins and the genes have been coupled together by a transducer, implying that this living being was and is recognizably (and even very highly) intelligent. We can read confirmation of this intelligence in the nature of the genetic code, which is a creative symbolic language – the ultimate hallmark of an intelligent Being.

The universe had an origin and so life had to have had an origin as well. We have already deduced that the origin of life is the supreme ordering event of all that has followed. The genesis of life gave rise to gene-directed life, which in turn gave rise to gene-directed evolution – the most complex ordering phenomenon ever uncovered by humankind. Biological evolution in turn generated the intelligent human mind. Yet in the beginning there were no genes. The symbolic creative language of the genes had to be fabricated by an intelligent Being, prior to the origin of life itself on planet Earth.

Now we can see that the trail of intelligence, from humanity through evolution to the genesis of life, reaches out beyond the origin of life itself. This is the crucial step. Once we have seen an extra-universal intelligence, we must see a living Mind to go with it. This Mind is the mind of the universe. God exists.

---

1 This is to account for the relatively straight hydrogen bonds that can form between bases.
2 For a more comprehensive introduction and still quite understandable treatment here, see M. Denton, *Evolution: A Theory in Crisis* (Bethesda, Md.: Adler and Adler, 1986), ch. 10.
3 See Ibid., ch. 11, for a more comprehensive discussion of the ribosome problem.
4 See Ibid., 266.
5 See F. Crick, *Life Itself* (New York: Simon and Shuster, 1981), 46, 143.

A Glimpse of the Creator at Work

Now that we have reached the end of the trail in our searching for a Creator, we can only look back and remember the high points of the trip. I noted at the very beginning that "does God exist?" is both the ultimate philosophical question and the ultimate subject of this book. And I noted at the very end of the last chapter that, at the end of my exploration of what contemporary science has to say on the subject, the answer is yes: God exists. "What would a summary of the argument in a few thousand words or less look like?" is the final question I want to address now, by way of conclusion, at the very end of the book.

We can start with the proposition that a natural phenomenon must contain within itself its own explanation. And then we can add the parallel proposition that if a natural phenomenon does not contain its own explanation, it must have a supernatural explanation. Philosophy prohibits the deduction of the higher order of being from the lower order. To prove the existence of a Creator, one must demonstrate the necessity of a higher-order parameter in the affairs of the universe. Intelligence is the variable of choice, and so one must demonstrate that intelligence is necessary to complete the explanation of natural phenomena. Intelligence is housed in the mind. Human intelligence is real and unambiguous. And thus the task is to causally link the reality of human intelligence to a prior intelligence – the intelligence of a Creator. One must show that the prior intelligence of a Creator is necessary to complete a rational account of the universe, that conforms with the evidence which science presents.

In fact, contemporary science does assert that the universe had a beginning. The moment of the big bang was the time in the universe when there was no 'before.' The legendary opening words of the Genesis narrative in the Judaeo-Christian Bible, for instance, predict that there was an "In the beginning...", and science now shows that indeed there was. The eternal universe is dead. All physical properties are derivatives of the creative event of the big bang. Space, matter, energy, and the laws of physics are all derivatives of this first creative moment. It turns out that the fundamental forces of nature are precisely balanced, and we can say that it is in the nature of the universe to evolve complex worlds. Physical evolution has a purpose: a complex creature needs a complex home. The universe has every appearance of having been deliberately designed to evolve a home for such a complex creature as modern humanity.

Within the universe the natural biological process of evolution has generated the human mind. The universe has no knowledge of this mind it has generated, but the human mind knows the universe. We no longer worry about how the universe can be explained: now the question is how to explain the science that explains the universe. How do the abstract thoughts of science and mathematics succeed in understanding the physical world? Implicit in the very success of science is the suggestion of an overarching mental order to the universe. Mental order on the stupendous scale of the cosmos requires an equally stupendous scale of mind – and this is the Mind of a Creator. Arguing that it takes Intelligence to beget intelligence, we can say that the abstract inquiries of science have been probing a few of the thought processes of the Creator. Having linked the mind of humanity to the Mind of the Creator at the cosmic level, we must go on to show that the evolution of human intelligence was a deliberate act.

The four terrestrial classes of vertebrates – fish, amphibians, reptiles, and mammals – exhibit an unambiguous evolutionary sequence of increased brain size. The mammals are the brainiest creatures on Earth. Within the mammals the primates exhibit an accelerated trend of increasing brain size: the primates are the brainiest of all the mammals. Within the primates the rate of growth in brain size increases dramatically in the extinct hominids. And modern humankind is the brainiest creature of all. The implication is that the process of biological evolution pursued a planned program of brain enlargement, to provide the physical housing and intellectual machinery for the human mind that was ultimately to emerge.

The contention that evolution has been in the business of generating intelligence deliberately gains support from the "excess intelligence" shown by the gorilla and the chimpanzee. Over a 2-million-year period the huge brains of the extinct hominids merely resulted in a desultory collection of crude stone implements. Extinct hominids possessed an enormous neural machine, but they failed in a rather spectacular fashion to put it to any great use. The modern human mind that has built medicine, art, philosophy, religion, morality, science, and technology is only now getting up to speed. It took 50,000 years of trial and error for humanity to begin unlocking the secrets in its own head. So we can see that the human brain was intellectually orders of magnitude in excess of any demands that were imposed on it in the Stone Age. Human intelligence was a preadaptation: it was an anticipation of the needs of the future rather than a response to the needs of the past.

The very physique of humankind befits an intelligent creature and none other. The loss of physical strength, the nakedness, and the absence of a season of female heat are all 'reduced-animal' characteristics, that compel humankind to learn and build cultural order. And so as well the brain is adapted to learn by the suppression of neuron replication. Evolution developed speech centres in the brain, while simultaneously developing the physical organs of speech. The wide range of controlled sounds necessary for language are generated by the vocal chords, which were late developments in hominid history and probably restricted to modern humanity. All these physical traits were 'feedback' that catalyzed intellectual development.

The deanimalized physique of modern humanity was the key that unlocked the neurological surplus in the brain. But a large unused neural capacity had to be developed *before* the self-conscious awakening took place. If the ancestral hominids had used their brains to full capacity, they would have exhausted the Earth's resources before we had any chance to evolve. A gradual development of intelligence would have imprisoned humanity in the Stone Age forever. To avoid this pre-emption of human destiny, evolution generated in the hominids three times the size of brain and an exponential explosion of neural complexity in just 5 million years. All the evidence points to the conclusion that the form and shape of humanity was pre-determined long before the first human being ever emerged. Biological evolution fashioned human intelligence purposefully and followed an intelligent design.

All the living organisms alive today are beautifully adapted to their environment. The fossils of ancient life also exhibit near-perfect adaptation. There is no reason to challenge the contention that all of the 1 to 3 billion species which ever existed were marvellously adapted to their environment. On the contrary the evidence implies a stupendously successful evolutionary process, that must be viewed as a characteristic of life over geological time. Intellectually, only two propositions can explain such biological evolution: the first says that evolution is the tool of an intelligent Designer, and hence will produce such intelligent results as near-perfect designs; the second says that evolution is a self-ordering process based on contingent mutations that can also produce near-perfect designs. The great discriminator between these two explanations is that contingent processes, if they were to be rerun, would not in all statistical likelihood arrive at the same result more than once.

Yet nature has contrived to rerun the experiment and arrive at the same result a number of times. Myxobacteria and slime moulds have both produced stalks and fruiting bodies from initially autonomous individuals. All the ancient birds with jaws and teeth evolved descendants with a keratinous beak.

The terrestrial reptiles and mammals produced two marine porpoise-type organisms capable of live birth – both of which have left no evidence of transitional forms. The mammals have produced many convergences, such as two groups of monkeys and two porcupines. Pride of place goes to the marsupials and the placentals: the less numerous marsupials have produced only two genuinely distinctive organisms, while both groups have generated nearly identical wolves. Across the great divide in the animal kingdom, with the echinoderms and chordates on one side and virtually all other animals on the other, the mollusks and the vertebrates have produced almost identically designed eyes. In these as in other senses, the "test for contingency" has failed again and again.

Similarly, spectacular evidence of deliberate results in biological evolution lies at the base of the Cambrian period, some 575 million years ago. At this point four of the most complex animal phyla appear simultaneously and abruptly, and each introduces the same innovation into biology. The soft-bodied ancestors of each phylum are completely retooled, so as to incorporate a skeleton as part of their fundamental anatomy. None of the phyla have any skeletonized ancestors. Genetic retooling on such a scale, occurring simultaneously in four phyla of organisms, can only be explained as a response to some global stimulus.

In fact it seems that the soft-bodied ancestors of these phyla were responding to a global increase in oxygen. That they all got into the business of incorporating a skeleton in their blueprint must signal some predisposition to do so. These organisms were predisposed to evolve a skeleton when the environment permitted – a case of unambiguous preadaptation and design. Evolution anticipated the arrival of an oxygen-rich environment before any such thing actually existed on the Earth. Anticipation is intellectual in nature, and this implies that evolution is the tool of an intelligent Designer who has fashioned intelligent designs.

And so, too, biologists, in struggling to deal with overwhelming amounts of data, have inadvertently uncovered a natural hierarchy to life. All the higher ranks of the biological classification system are isolated. There are no cross-linkages: every member of a particular rank is equally representative of that rank as any other member. Intelligent human beings also construct hierarchies to facilitate information flow and decision-making. And the natural hierarchy of biology is confirmed by protein analysis. Proteins are under the control of the genes, and genes are full of information. The natural hierarchy of biology is a genetic master blueprint of life. The evidence signals that evolution is the most systematic and complex ordering phenomenon ever uncovered by human beings, and this phenomenon leads directly to human intelligence. Systematic and complex ordering is the hallmark of an intelligent Being at work. Again we see the intelligent Designer and "His" intelligent Designs.

Life, itself, arose as one single cell – the Eve, as it were, to all life in the future. Life has continued uninterrupted for over 3.5 billion years. Yet the individual cells of life are constantly turning over and over and over again in the cellular duplication process. Life today is as vital as it ever was, and this bears witness to the stringent accuracy of the copying mechanism within the genes. Indeed the accuracy of the duplication process in the genes can quite reasonably be described as no less than miraculous. And over 3.5 billion years, life has evolved into a spectacular array of diverse organisms, culminating with the self-conscious human being. It is a contradiction to attribute evolution, the most complex ordering phenomenon ever discovered, to an accumulation of errors in the miraculously accurate copying mechanism within the genes. Biologists are quite incapable of demonstrating anything near the required number of errors or mutations in the copying system of living organisms.

There is far more information in the genes of humankind than in a bacterium. Not only do physical organisms grow but the genes grow as well. There exists no *a priori* reason to interpret the growth of information in the genes as contingent while all other less complex manifestations of biological growth such as embryology are utterly systematic. Life is characterized by systematic complexity and the roots of this complexity – in the evolutionary process – must themselves be both systematic and complex.

The similarity of genes and proteins shared by all living organisms implies one initial living cell. With all its evolutionary adventures, life is firmly locked into one type and format of genetic expression. The origin of life has to be a unique event. And unique events do not repeat themselves and can never be verified or falsified. And so there are no compelling scientific reasons to hold that life could have an inorganic origin. The hypothesis is based on an axiom or a belief (or even its own blind faith).

In fact the traditional reductionism of Darwinist philosophy, which is so attached to the spontaneous-origin-of-life hypothesis, contrives to contradict three key scientific findings. It insists that there were "simple" transitional life forms, which were not dependent on photosynthesis. Yet science has found nothing simpler than a bacterium, and the vast majority of living things do depend on photosynthesis, directly or indirectly. Reductionism insists that life must have had an inorganic origin. But contemporary science has repeatedly confirmed the biogenesis principle: only living things can generate other living things. And science has found biological death irreversible. Yet the spontaneous inorganic origin of life implies that it is not.

Alongside these scientific contradictions, reductionist philosophy is caught in a self-made paradox about photosynthesis. Since a photosynthesizing organism is infinitely too complex to have been the first living cell, a simpler type of cell is postulated. Yet the simpler fermenting organism must logically starve to death in the absence of photosynthesis. There is no resolution to this conundrum. The energy logic of life, as we know it, demands a great engine to maintain a cyclical flow of oxygen, hydrogen, and carbon through the biological world. Photosynthesis is that great engine and without it life would starve.

A long list of arguments can be advanced to illustrate the enormity of the problems involved in the spontaneous-origin-of-life hypothesis. Generating pure compounds in the contamination of the Archaean is an absolute mystery: no geochemical hypothesis on the subject has even been attempted. Separating right- from left-handed molecules in the formation of proteins and nucleotides is another mystery. To this we must add the problem of the scarcity of useful proteins and the over-abundance of useless proteins. Somehow these proteins as well as the genetic molecules must be synthesized inorganically in dehydration reactions in the presence of water, even though hydration (the opposite type of reaction) is predicted to occur.

None of these problems has ever been resolved to any significant degree. The chief among them all is the ribosome problem: accurate proteins are required to generate accurate proteins. This poses the same logical dilemma as the paradox of the chicken and the egg, and it cannot be resolved. Today we ought to be able to see how the concept of the spontaneous origin of life finally leads us into a strange garden, where the laws of science appear to break down.

Gene-directed biological evolution is the most systematic and complex ordering phenomenon ever discovered. Life had an origin and whatever generated the genes in the first place must be the supreme ordering phenomenon of all. In the end, contemporary science has no explanation. And the result is an intellectual vacuum that begs to be filled. Nobody wants to argue for a God of the gaps. Yet if there is a God in nature there will be some very substantial gaps. And this *is* the situation in which we seem to find ourselves today.

We are not in a position of having to argue that the origin of life is the sole 'discontinuity' or 'singularity.' Science is confronted by two imponderable questions of this sort. What caused the big bang and what is responsible for the origin of life? It is the combination of the purposeful physical evolution of the universe and the intelligibility of the universe that allows us to posit the existence of the Mind of the universe in the first place. The spontaneous-origin-of-life hypothesis has failed. This failure allows us invoke the default hypothesis of biogenesis – life begets life. The origin of life flows from another living entity.

As it happens, I would argue, we can actually corroborate this conclusion. All the biochemical processes in nature exhibit high levels of control over spontaneity. (The copying process of the genes, for example, has a built-in correcting feature.) The only analogue for this control over spontaneity is the control exhibited by modern human technology. Control is consistent with the workings of intelligence since it requires continuous information.

One of the greatest control processes in biology is photosynthesis, which harnesses the sun's energy, splits water, reduces carbon dioxide, and serves as the engine room of life. Thermodynamic analysis shows that photosynthesis cannot have arisen spontaneously: the entire process is irreducibly complex. A factor of intelligence is required to explain impossible statistics and the crossing of infinite entropy barriers. The process needs information from somewhere to work.

When genes and photosynthesis are coupled together, the scale of the design becomes breathtaking. All the evidence, such as it is, points to the conclusion that the first organism was a photosynthesizing bacterium. This organism set out to tame the planet and to prepare it for future evolutionary adventures among the multicellular organisms three billion years later. Forward planning on this scale befits a Mind of the universe and nothing less. Biological evolution runs on a time scale vastly beyond that of the participating organisms.

This point is reinforced by the accuracy of the gene-copying in nuclear cells. The participating organisms operate on a time-scale of days while their copying system is still accurate after 1.5 billion years. The individual organisms that evolved the copying system had no personal need for this level of accuracy. This accuracy is a preadaptation for life's longevity and it occurs on a breathtaking scale, just like photosynthesis.

The logic of biology reduces to the logic of the information in the genes. Genes are the brains of the living cell and proteins are the muscles. But the genes and the proteins are independent chemical systems. They cannot be reduced to each other. The ribosome that connects the operation of the genes and the proteins is by definition a transducer: it couples two independent systems. The factor of intelligence implied by thermodynamics supports the conclusion that the use of a transducer is evidence of intelligence in its own right.

At the very end we come to the genes themselves. Building on the factor of intelligence indicated by thermodynamics, and the transducer of the ribosome, we can say that genes are made up of a creative symbolic language. The language of the genes is so economical that the sum of human knowledge could easily be written in the chemistry of genetics, and all of it would fit comfortably in a teaspoon. Creative symbolic languages are artifacts of the abstractions of an intelligent mind. The supreme ordering event that gave rise to the first gene-directed cell had to involve the generation of the first genes. This event occurred before the origin of life on Earth, since the first genes had to exist as components before they became integral parts of the living cell. We now have an unbroken chain, from human intelligence all the way back to the origin of life and beyond. An Intelligence existed prior to the origin of life.

Intelligence is a characteristic of life alone. Human intelligence is a reality and it is connected by an unbroken evolutionary chain back to the first living cell of genesis. Over geological history evolution is a characteristic of life and it has functioned intelligently throughout its long regime. The great hierarchy of biology attests powerfully to this point. Thus we can expand the biogenesis principle by saying that it takes intelligent life to beget intelligent life. We are now able to connect the supreme ordering event of the origin of life with the Mind of the universe. But the universe itself is intelligible. It possesses a mental order, and it, too, had an origin. The First life is both intelligent and extra-universal. God exists.

To come down very quickly from such heights with a sort of footnote, I have one utterly final thought on the widest implications of this kind of argument. Throughout our small planet we increasingly live in a world that shows some great thirst for the spiritual dimension of life. Yet for several generations now we have also felt that the truly remarkable achievements of the contemporary scientific enterprise (which is, above all else, the great intellectual engine of the technology we all so admire and want to use) have cast a kind of darkness on this thirst, and fundamentally called into question its claims to intellectual credibility.

At the bottom of everything, what I have been most concerned to show here is that this is just not true. In fact, the spiritual dimension of life has been crucial to our progressive evolution – and even, ultimately, to the growth of our present technology. Questing after this dimension ought to be judged a more credible pursuit than a few very clever people of the nineteenth century once imagined, for a brief moment in time. If what I have struggled to do in these pages can help a few readers achieve some liberation in this respect today, I will feel entitled to believe that my journey which began on the Archaean rocks of the Canadian Shield has evolved some intelligent purpose of its own.

INDEX

A

Adaptation
  feather, 67
  keratin,67
  perfection, 65, 66, 120, 121, 178,185
  viper fangs, 65
Adenine, 170
Adenosine triphosphate (ATP), 104
Adenosine monophosphate (AMP), 104
Adenosine diphosphate (ADP), 104
Aestivation, 70
Agriculture, 46, 50, 51
Agriculture
  degradation of soil, 56
  mathematics, 50
  Mayan, 56
  primitive, 56
  salt in California and Babylon, 56
American bison, 69
Amino acids
  Archaean, 137, 138
  folding of chain, 172
  left handed, 137, 138
  proteins, 167, 170
Amphibians, 21
Animal kingdom, division of, 94
Antarctic whale, 69
Apes, 58
Apes, excess intellectual capacity, 38, 60
Aquinas, Saint Thomas, 5, 18
Archaean, 1
Archaean
  amino acids, 137, 138
  autocatalyst, 160
  availability of nucleotides, 134
  availability of amino acids, 134
  Canadian Shield, 190
  components for life, 134
  conditions, 131
  contamination, 2, 131, 137, 139, 142, 151
  difficulty synthesizing protein, 141
  environment, 130, 131, 150, 157
  hostility to life, 135
  iron, 2
  origin of life, 2, 132, 137
  Phosphorous, 2, 141, 163

  prebiotic soup, 134
  protecting autocatalyst, 151
  protein synthesis, 2
  self-ordering systems, 152
Arctic tern, 69
Aristotle, 106
Arthropods (trilobite), 103
Australian aborigines, 52

B

Bats, 83
Beetle, 178
Behaviour, 79
Behe, Michael, 101, 163
  irreducible complexity, 68, 97, 100, 101
Bergson, Henri, 144, 164
Bible, "In the beginning ... ," 1, 183
Bible, Genesis, 5
Big bang, 5, 64, 183
  model, 7
  act of creation, 18
  hot model and Creator, 8
  inflation model, 7
  neutrons, 11
  origin of the universe, 6
  protons, 11
  residual radiation, 6
  singularity, 6
Biogenesis principle, 3, 62, 98, 123, 143, 145
Biogenesis principle
  creator, 160
  origin of life, 181
  intelligence, 190
Biological classification
  birds, 107
  equal representation in ranks, 111
  genes, 112, 120
  hierarchy, 111, 106, 109, 119, 120, 186
  higher ranks, 31
  Homo genus, 39, 42
  Homo sapiens, 52, 107
  isolation of ranks, 110, 111, 113, 114, 120
  links (Archaeopteryx), 113
  master blueprint, 112, 116, 120, 121,186
  natural order, 108, 110